EAT
WELL
LOSE
WEIGHT
GET
HEALTHY

SARAH SKELTON

Recipes created by Sarah Skelton
Designed by Alice Brown
Production director: Sarah Skelton
Photography of Sarah Skelton by Alisha Giles

Publisher: Independent Publishing Network.
Publication date: 2019
ISBN: 9781789725490

Email: info@healthylivingwithsarah.com
Website: www.healthylivingwithsarah.com

Printed in United Kingdom

Publisher's notes:
While every care has been taken in compiling the recipes for this book, Sarah Skelton, or any other persons who have been involved in working on this publication, cannot accept responsibility for any errors or omissions, inadvertent or not, that may be found in the recipes or text, not for any problems that may arise as a result of preparing one of these recipes or following the eating plan. If you are pregnant or breastfeeding, suffered with a eating disorder or have any special dietary requirements or medical conditions, it is advisable to consult a medical professional before following the eating plan and any of the recipes contained in this book.

Contents

Acknowledgements

I'd like to thank Alice Brown for all her hard work in designing this book. For listening to my endless twittering on about the concept and for putting up with me tweaking the page positioning!

A massive thank you goes to my husband Andrew, for his continued support and belief in me to achieve my goals and for putting up with my obsession in writing this book.

To Rosemary Conley CBE, for giving me a chance to make a difference!

To all my trialists, who took the plan in its raw form and tested it, with great results!

And finally, thank you to everyone who came to my classes over the years. You taught me so much about empathy, friendship and determination.

Welcome to Eat Well, Lose Weight, Get healthy!

My name is Sarah,

I hope you love this book and learn to see that it is much more than about losing weight. I want to inspire you to look at food in a positive light, to get creative in the kitchen and love food the way it's meant to be loved!

I've over 21 years in the weight management and fitness industry as a nutritionist and fitness instructor. I've been privileged to work alongside some of the most distinguished people within this sector, I've written several diets under a well-known brand and published my first recipe book, packed full of healthier recipes for one in 2019.

You need to know I love food, I mean **REALLY** love food and everything it stands for. I've struggled with my weight for years, and I've helped literally thousands of men and women become slimmer, fitter and healthier during that time too. My struggle with my own weight really means I've been able to empathise with anyone trying to lose weight. It doesn't matter whether it's 4lbs or 40 lbs, to each of us our own struggle can feel like a mountain.

So, I went back to basics, looked at what I know people dislike about the whole weight-loss journey, what I did and didn't like myself. Added to that I factored in my own expertise in the field and my love of food and voila I lost 2 stones in 8 weeks, felt so much better, slept better, had more energy and I am more mentally alert than I've been in years! I started a trial with a small group of people, with combined weight, health and mental health backgrounds to see how they found it. And, yes it worked – it really worked!! You'll see some of their quotes scattered throughout this book.

This book is more than just losing weight, I hope the recipes inspire you to cook more and be generally healthier in both body and mind. Remember you can achieve anything with a bit of positivity!

Enjoy the journey!

PS Take a look at my website where I share some of my recipes, have my blog and much more. – www.healthylivingwithsarah.com

Does the plan really work?

The answer is yes, but only if you want it too. You need to accept and understand that you need to make changes to the way you eat to achieve your aim, whether that be weight loss or just about eating healthier. If your answer is "yes I am ready, but...." then, you are likely to struggle as 'but' is already putting a negative influence towards the outcome.

Please don't take that to mean that you will fail, absolutely not! It means you have to think about why you want to do this. Does taking this action mean more to you than eating something that's not good for you or not exercising?

So there are a few things we can do to make sure our behavioural change is a continual and straightforward process.

Firstly, try as much as you can to remove yourself from situations that may tempt you. For example, if you walk to work and walk past a bakery that's wafting out the smells of freshly baked bread, sausage rolls and more. You can't help but nip in and pick up a little something for lunch. Using a different route will help to minimise the action of just 'popping in'. Making a packed lunch the night before means your brain already knows you have lunch. Invariably creating a packed lunch is much cheaper than buying ready-made. We very rarely only buy the one thing when we visit a shop. Being prepared by taking our lunch to work really helps and stops you being caught into buying a meal-deal with that little extra something you don't need.

A great way to understand if our eating habits are triggered by an event, emotional change or circumstance is to keep a written track of the foods we eat. You should include when they were eaten and how you felt at the time. This is by no means essential, but if you are struggling to make those changes, you so desperately want to achieve, then this is the perfect thing to try. It's called self-monitoring, and it will help you to identify if there is a pattern that causes you to choose foods that may not be helping you to get to your goal. If there is a pattern, then you can look to see if you can find some simple solutions to avoid those triggers in the future.

It's interesting to realise that we all add association of emotional stimuli at some point in our lives. For me it was a touch too much Crème de Menthe at the age of 16, it took me years to be able to eat a Polo mint, and even now I can't look at a bottle of the stuff without feeling slightly green! By the same token, macaroons make me smile, and cheese is my comfort food, so I control those foods because those are ones I know I have to be wary of, especially in severe/emotional times.

Take time to think about foods that you love or dislike and identify why they affect you in that way. It will go a long way to helping you make sustainable changes. Don't fall into the common mistake of banning the foods you love for fear of falling off the wagon; instead, try practising self-control. It sounds easy, it's not, but you can do it with a little self-belief and motivation. Remember everything in moderation!

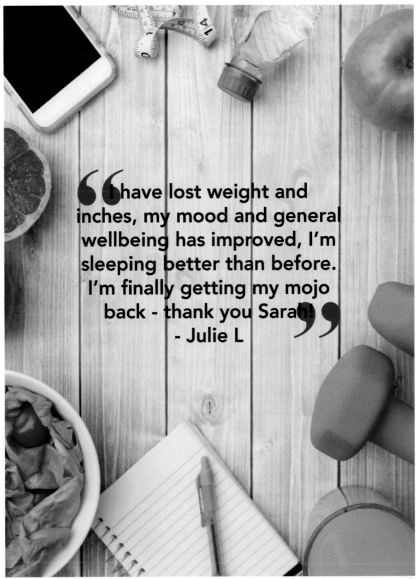

66 I have lost weight and inches, my mood and general wellbeing has improved, I'm sleeping better than before. I'm finally getting my mojo back - thank you Sarah! **99**
- **Julie L**

Where are the calories?

You will have discovered that there is no mention of counting calories within this healthy eating plan. That's not because they don't matter, because they do. This program has been devised so that you don't need to worry about them to lose weight and get healthier. Your energy intake is being moderated by using portion control following the principles on page **13**.

Over the last 21 years, I have helped thousands of people to lose weight. The most common issue is that very few people like counting calories, it's a pain, sometimes time-consuming and just dull! However, weight loss is simple, we need to eat less and exercise more to get the right balance for our body.

It's much easier to think about food as a portion than a specific number. It takes the emphasis off "I'm on a diet" and replaces it with "I'm eating healthier". That means it's seen less like a chore and more as a sustainable way of life. This has always been my aim.

I'm by no means knocking calorie counting because, for many it works, they like the structure and the feeling of safety in the numbers. But merely counting calories or following a low GI plan does not mean healthy options are always taken. For example, chocolate has a lower GI than many healthier options, but if you eat a 1,000 calories of it a day, then your body won't thank you after a while.

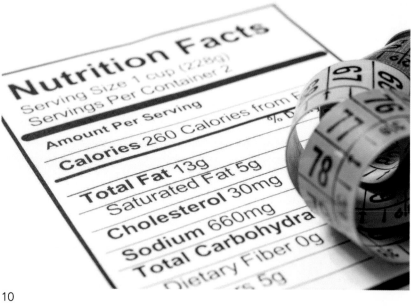

Carbohydrate free?

You will see that I have included carbohydrates in this plan as they are essential to maintaining a healthy body. Yes, you can lose weight quickly by following a virtually carb-free diet (this usually is less than 30g of carbs per day). It's not suitable for general health over a more extended term. This plan is all about the bigger picture, it's not a quick fix, it's a permanent one!

It's not a carb-heavy plan either. It's perfect if you are pre-diabetic and are working towards a better blood sugar balance, or if you have Type 2 Diabetes. One of my trialists, who is a Type 2 on insulin, found that her sugar balance improved dramatically, and she needed to take less medication as a result.

If you have diabetes or any condition where changing your eating habits may affect your health, then you should speak to a medical practitioner before starting.

If you need to track your carbs and sugar intake, you will find that all of my recipes in this book and on my website contain nutritional information per serving to help you make more informed choices.

What do I eat?

You will find there is a 21 day suggested plan included in this book. This plan has been created to get you on the right track. However, the whole concept of this plan is to get you thinking more about the foods you eat, show you good food can be made quickly and cost-effectively.

For this reason, if you adopt the basic principles outlined in this section, you will be able to choose and create your own meals if you wish. There are over 110 recipes included within this book, so there is plenty to keep your taste buds excited. Don't forget you can visit **www.healthylivingwithsarah.com** for even more great recipes or adapt some of your favourites to make them healthier.

In the 21-day plan, you will see there are options for meat-eaters, vegetarians and vegans.

Principles:

Where possible, keep a maximum of a nine-hour window between your first meal and the last one of the day. It will help to keep your body ticking over, rather than going for more extended periods between meals.

Breakfast: Choose a higher fibre option as this will keep hunger at bay until you are ready for your lunch. Breakfast can be as late as 10 am if that works for you, there's no need to have it at 7.30am if that does not suit your lifestyle.

Lunch: This should have a higher protein level, but not free of carbohydrates. It means your sugar levels are more likely to stay stable throughout the afternoon, meaning you'll be more alert and the need to pick between meals will diminish.

Dinner: This should be a balanced meal, containing carbohydrates, protein and a little fat. Avoid ready-made meals, if you do have them keep to one per week and bulk up with veg and no potatoes.

Snacks: These need to be higher in protein and complex carbohydrates. Have no more than one-two snacks between meals per day, ideally one or none! You will find a suggested snack list at the end of the 21-day meal plan incase you need something.

Five a day – you should aim for a minimum of five portions of fruit and vegetables per day (except for ordinary potatoes which are not included within this). Avoid having more than two portions of fruit each day to control your sugar intake. One portion is very roughly equal to 80g in weight. See page **26** for a guide to fruit and vegetable portion sizes. Fruit, vegetable juices and smoothies should be kept to one glass per day – max 150ml to control the amount of sugar consumed.

Basic portion sizes per person for the main meal:

Carbohydrates
• Pasta (70g dry weight)
• Rice (60g dry weight)
• Couscous (50g dry weight)
• Lentils/Pulses (50g dry weight)
• Quinoa (50-55g dry weight)
• Sweet Potato(160-180g- raw weight)
• Ordinary potatoes (150-160g raw weight)

Protein
• 100-120g beef, lean steak or mince
• 150-160g chicken breast or Turkey (without skin)
• 100-120g lean pork
• 100-120g lean lamb
• 200g any white fish
• 150g any shellfish such as prawns
• 120-140g salmon fillet
• 160g cooked weight lentils or chickpeas
• 160g meat-free products, such as Quorn
• 3 medium eggs

BREAD: Choose multigrain, stoneground brown bread, or rye bread - avoid white bread. If you suffer from gluten intolerance, use a gluten-free alternative. Bread should only be consumed once per day, so if you have toast for breakfast, then avoid a sandwich for lunch or a slice with dinner. All bread should be a medium slice. There is no need to buy 'slimming bread' on this plan; I recommend you don't. One medium bread roll or a slice of bread should be about 35g

BREAKFAST CEREALS: Choose oat-based or high-fibre varieties, e.g. Porridge, Shreddies, no-added sugar or salt muesli or cereals containing natural grains (such as Shredded Wheat and Weetabix). Portion sizes should be 35-40g

OILY FISH: For good heart health, it is essential to try and eat two portions of fish per week, ideally one of which should be oily fish – e.g. mackerel, salmon, sardines, herrings. If you are vegetarian, vegan, or don't like oily fish you need to ensure that you eat foods rich in omega 3 fatty acids such as chia seeds, rapeseed oil, algal oil, hemp seed, walnuts, flaxseeds and even Brussels sprouts! Adding chia and flax seeds to your breakfast is one of the simplest ways to achieve this, 1tsp per day will help

RICE: Use basmati rice where possible as this has less effect on your blood sugar levels than regular white rice and therefore helps to keep your blood sugars slightly more stable after eating. Keep your portion size for rice to 60g dry weight for dinner. (30-40g for lunch).

PASTA: Use dry or fresh; ideally brown, lentil or buckwheat based – if not ordinary pasta is perfectly fine. Max serving size is 70g dry weight for a dinner. (30-40g for lunch).

DRINKS: You should aim to have 6 - 8 glasses of fluids per day. Tea, coffee and sugar-free drinks can form part of this. Staying hydrated is key to helping your body function properly.

COOKING: Rapeseed oil in spray form is perfect, as it controls the amount of fat used. It's incredibly versatile as it can be used cold and in shallow frying without compromise. It contains the least amount of saturated fat of all oils. One to try is Red Palm Fruit & Rapeseed oil mix, beautiful colour, great flavour and packed full of good things and it's a fantastic source of omega 3, 6 and 9. It contains more omega 3 than olive oil.

NUTS & SEEDS: Nuts and seeds are fine as long as you control your intake and have just one portion per day – which is about 25g. Brazils, walnuts, hazelnuts are good choices as they contain the least amount of carbohydrates compared to other nuts.

ALCOHOL: Avoid alcohol where possible and if you do have a drink keep it to no more than two units per day (maximum of 14 units per week), aim for two to three alcohol-free days per week.

CHEESE: Use reduced-fat options where possible and control the portion size; no more than 30g of cheese per person per meal.

EATING OUT: Limit eating out to once a week, and choose sensibly. Be realistic and understand that often, restaurants don't have a perfect choice, and that's fine – you are dining out as a treat! Never be frightened to ask for slight changes to a meal, i.e. no sauce, less cream etc. Don't starve yourself before or after the meal, be more active instead and walk an extra 30 minutes the next day.

A no frills or gimmicks healthy eating plan , using delicious recipes that the whole family can enjoy or making own recipes following advice. I lost weight and inches without really trying, whilst feeling more energised and much better generally.
- Marlene B

Eat plenty of fibre

As adults we should be aiming to eat 30g of fibre per day. Eating this amount of fibre on a regular basis will help to:

• Lower cholesterol levels
• Reduce the risk of bowel cancer
• Helps constipation
• May help to reduce blood pressure through the benefits of reducing cholesterols levels
• Keep you feeling fuller for longer

Finding ways to increase your fibre intake can be difficult, below are some suggestions to help you achieve your goal. You will find all of the recipes within this book state how much fibre each serving contains to help you achieve the required 30g per day.

• Try to introduce high fibre breakfast cereals into your diet.
• Aim for 5 pieces of fruits and vegetables every day. They are low in calories and full of fibre to give that fuller feeling for longer
• Eat fruits and vegetables raw where possible. Boiling can result in a loss of up to one-half of the fibre in the water, so consider steaming or stir-frying to retain more fibre.
• Try adding fresh or dried fruit, nuts or seeds on top of your breakfast cereal.
• Add bran to muffins, breads and casseroles.
• Try to have baked, wedged or boiled potatoes with the skin on to be eaten hot or cold.
• Go for wholemeal or wholegrain/multigrain bread instead of white bread.
• Try wholemeal or lentil based pasta, bulgur wheat or brown rice instead of white pasta and white rice. Remember, brown rice does take longer to cook than white rice so give yourself plenty of time when you first use it.
• Add beans and lentils to salads, soups and stews. Consider beans on toast as a light meal or try some salads with added kidney beans, chickpeas and butterbeans.
• Add vegetables to sauces, stews or curries.
• For snacks try fruit or vegetable sticks, unsalted nuts or seeds.

Fluids

So, we all know we should drink plenty, but actually doing it can be hard.

Adults should be aiming for 6-8 glasses of fluids every day, under normal conditions. When we exercise, the weather gets hotter etc. then we need to increase our intake accordingly.

We must hydrate over some time, rather than in bouts as this can overload our kidneys, so consistency and frequency are key.

It goes without saying that water is the best option for us, and below are just a few of the reasons why:

- It's cheap, you don't need to buy bottled water, especially in the UK.
- It helps to regulate our appetite
- Improves digestion
- Eliminates harmful toxins and substances, such as alcohol
- Helps to reduce blood pressure
- Contributes to reducing water retention
- Helps to strengthen our bladder function
- Maintains our kidney function
- Helps to keep the moisture in our skin
- Helps to ease joint pain
- Boosts our energy levels
- Reduces the risk of bowel cancer

Research shows that thirst and hunger sensations are often triggered together. When we experience a slight drop in our hydration levels, as little as 2%, our brain sometimes sends out a false impression of hunger. This makes us contemplate eating food when actually what we really need are fluids. This is very important, particularly when you are trying to lose or maintain your weight. So, whenever you feel hungry, always have a drink first so that you know your body is getting the fluid it requires to function correctly.

It's not all about drinking water, other forms of fluids are okay too. Tea, coffee, milk, fruit juices and soft drinks are all excellent, although fruit juices should be restricted to 150ml per day and all soft drinks should be sugar-free. Water is also contained in everyday foods you eat, and on average 20% of total fluid intake comes from dietary intake at mealtimes

What happens when we started to get a little dehydrated?

Consistent dehydration can cause;
• Constipation
• Kidney stones and gallstones
• Pressure ulcers

Dehydration can also cause us to become mentally impaired;
• Headaches
• Dizzy spells
• Tiredness
• Reduce levels of concentration and alertness

Tips on how to boost your fluid intake:

• Drink after visiting the toilet.
• Carry a bottle with you at all times to increase access.
• Start your day with a glass of water and a slice of lemon. The lemon
  helps to flush out toxins that have built up in the body.
• Have water or a soft sugar free drink with each meal.
• Set goals for the number of glasses you aim to drink every day.
• Every time you drink coffee or tea also drink water.

Alcohol

Both men and women are advised not to drink more than 14 units a week regularly and to spread it over three or more days if regular consumption of 14 units a week is taken. One unit is 25mls of spirits, 75mls of wine, half a pint of ordinary strength lager, cider or beer.

When we drink alcohol, it increases the amount of water we lose from urination, thus resulting in dehydration. This is why if you do drink having a soft drink between alcoholic ones really helps.

From a weight gain perspective, it's not just about the energy or number of calories in any given drink. Our bodies are complex machines which can identify certain toxins such as alcohol. Because our body is pre-set to preserve life, it works on excreting the alcohol from our body as quickly as it can. This means any food, however healthy it may be, is converted into energy and sent straight to our fat stores, which can result in weight gain. So you can see restricting how much you drink will have a very positive impact on your waistline!

Tips on how to reduce alcohol intake:

- Avoid binge drinking
- Use a smaller glass.
- Do not drink on an empty stomach.
- Use low calorie/diet mixers to reduce your calorie intake further and to make your drinks last longer.
- Check the label as many drinks labels indicate how many units are contained.
- Don't eat snacks like crisps and peanuts with your drinks, the added salt will make you want to drink more and may raise your blood pressure.
- If you drink at home, buy a measure so that you know how much you are drinking.
- Keep a drinks diary, as writing this down regularly will help you to determine how much you're drinking.
- Try drinking each drink more slowly or alternating alcoholic beverages with soft or low alcohol ones.
- Have alcohol-free days, ideally three days per week

For many people having a drink at the end of a busy day, while cooking dinner or after the kids go to bed is a habit. Habits can be broken, but they take time, and you have to have alternative options in place.

For example, if a gin & tonic is your thing, try omitting the gin or using an alcohol-free gin alternative, use flavoured tonics and still add your ice and a slice of lemon or lime. You will even get the same feeling mainly if you use the same glass. This is because the eye will fool the brain into thinking it's part of your usual habit.

If lager or beer is your thing, then buy alcohol-free versions, keep them chilled, so you have one ready.

Get out of the habit of drinking because you are stressed or have nothing else to do. Look for other ways to relax. Activities like walking, having a nice bath, reading a book can help to distract your mind and feel better.

Remember it is just a habit, and habits can be broken!

Following a vegetarian or vegan lifestyle?

Being a vegetarian means you live on a diet of grains, pulses, nuts, seeds, vegetables and fruits with, or without, the use of dairy products and eggs. A vegetarian does not consume red meat, poultry, seafood and flesh of any other animal and this also includes omitting any animal by product such as animal fat or gelatin.

What type of vegetarian are you?

There is a variation between one person's interpretation of being a vegetarian to another, and this is due to personal preferences and reasons for following this type of diet.

If you are thinking of becoming vegetarian or following predominantly plant-based lifestyle then it is good to understand the various types.

- Semi-vegetarian: excludes red meat but will eat fish or poultry.
- Pescetarian: excludes red meat and poultry but will eat fish.
- Lacto-ovo vegetarian: does not eat any meat, poultry, fish, shellfish or ingredients derived e.g. gelatin and rennet. These vegetarians may also consume dairy products and eggs, but most likely only from free range origin.
- Ovo-vegetarians: include eggs but avoid all other animal foods, including dairy.
- Vegans: excludes all animal products including all derived additives and ingredients.
- Fruitarian: is a vegan, who restricts their diet to only consist of raw fruit and vegetables, nuts, seeds, pulses and grains.
- Macrobiotic: This is a pescetarian diet (sometimes vegetarian or vegan) fixed on ideas about types of food drawn from Zen Buddhism. Its focus is on foods that contain both the ying and yang (based on the Chinese philosophy). With seven levels that differ and increase in restriction with the lowest level being the most varied which includes fish but still excludes meat, eggs and dairy products. The highest level is based on only consuming brown rice.

When eliminating animal-based foods/products from your diet, there are some specific nutritional elements that you need to consider. The following factors are vital to staying healthy, and they must be integrated into your eating plan.

Iron

Normally we get most of our iron from red meat, which the body absorbs very easily. However, when red meat is removed from the diet then alternatives need to be sort.

Good alternative sources include:

• Wholemeal bread
• Dried fruit
• Fortified breakfast cereals
• Leafy green vegetables
• Nuts
• Beans and lentils
• Sesame seeds

Vitamin C

Vitamin C aids the absorption of iron into the bloodstream. As the body does not retain Vitamin C, you need to ensure you have a food that is rich in Vitamin C in the same meal that contains the source of iron. For example, having a small glass of orange juice with your breakfast cereal, adding peppers or broccoli to a meal. It's important to know that Vitamin C is depleted during the cooking process, so avoid overcooking foods.

Protein

As very few plant sources contain all the essential amino acids required by the body, except for soya, hemp and quinoa. It is vital that a vegetarian eats a mixture of different plant proteins to ensure that their nutritional requirements are met.

Good sources of protein for a vegetarian are:
• Seeds
• Nuts and nut butters (e.g. peanut butter)
• Soya and soya products e.g. soya dairy alternatives, tofu, soya nuts and soya mince
• Seitan and tempeh
• Grains such as wheat (found in cereals, pasta and bread), rice and maize
• Beans, lentils and chickpeas
• Milk and diary products such as cheese, but beware of the fat content, so always choose lower fat alternatives
• Eggs - **TIP** if you are following a vegan lifestyle a good replacement

for egg in recipes where the egg is used as a binding agent then mixing 1 tbsp of flaxmeal (ground flax seeds) with 3 tbsp of hot water, allow to cool, is the equivalent to using 1 egg.

Another source that some vegetarians may consume is Mycoprotein (such as Quorn) – some variations may not be suitable for vegans, so it is always best to check the label, as some variations contain egg.

Calcium

Is an essential mineral as it helps builds bones and teeth, promotes blood health, and is essential in the function of muscles and nerves.

For vegetarians not consuming dairy products, other sources include:

• Dried fruit: apricots and figs.
• Calcium-fortified foods e.g. soya milk, yoghurts and puddings.
• Sesame seeds and tahini.
• Brown and white bread.
• Calcium-set tofu (i.e. those prepared using calcium).
• Green leafy vegetable: Kale, collard, spinach etc.
• Nuts

Selenium

This helps protect cells and tissues from damage.
Good sources are:
• Brazil, cashew nuts and sunflower seeds
• Some fortified breakfast cereals
• Wheatgerm bread

Vitamin B12

Vitamin B12 is only found naturally in foods from animal sources and is essential in helping to build the genetic material of cells and production of blood cells. A vegetarian who does not eat eggs and dairy foods should consume fortified foods containing Vitamin B12.

• Vitamin B12 fortified yeast extract, such Marmite
• Vitamin B12 fortified breakfast cereals (with added vitamin B12)
• Vitamin B12 fortified dairy-free

A Guide to Portion sizes for Fruits and Vegetables

Adult portion size is equivalent to 80g.
(as eaten, edible portion, drained weight if canned)

VEGETABLES

Ackee (canned): 3 heaped tablespoons
Artichoke: 2 globe hearts
Asparagus: canned – 7 spears, fresh 5 spears
Aubergine: One third of an aubergine
Beans (cooked) – borlotti, black eye, broad, butter, cannellini, chickpeas, kidney, pinto, soya:
3 heaped tablespoons. Beans and pulses count as a maximum of one portion a day, however much you eat. This is because, while pulses contain fibre, they don't give the same mixture of vitamins, minerals and other nutrients as fruit and vegetables.
Beans (French/green/runner): 4 heaped tablespoons
Beetroot: bottled or fresh - 3 'baby' whole, or 7 slices
Broccoli: 2 spears, or 8 florets
Brussels sprouts: 6-8 Brussels sprouts
Butternut squash: 3 heaped tablespoons
Cabbage (cooked): 4 heaped tablespoons
Cabbage (shredded): 3 heaped tablespoons
Carrots: canned, fresh or shredded - 3 heaped tablespoons
Cauliflower: 8 florets
Celery: 1 stick
Chinese leaves (shredded): 4 heaped tablespoons
Courgettes: half a large courgette
Cucumber: 2-inch/5cm piece
Curly kale (cooked): 4 heaped tablespoons
Leeks: 1 medium leek (white part only)
Lentils: 3 tablespoons. Beans and pulses count as a maximum of one portion a day, however much you eat. This is because, while pulses contain fibre, they don't give the same mixture of vitamins, minerals and other nutrients as fruit and vegetables.
Lettuce (mixed leaves): 1 cereal/dessert bowl
Mange-Tout: one handful
Marrow (cooked and diced): 3 heaped tablespoons
Mixed veg (frozen): 3 tablespoons
Mushrooms: 14 button or 3-4 heaped tablespoons
Mushrooms (dried): 2 tablespoons
Okra: 9 medium
Onion: 1 medium
Pak Choi: 4 heaped tablespoons
Parsnips: 1 medium
Peas: fresh, frozen, canned - 3 heaped tablespoons

Pepper: half a pepper
Pumpkin (diced and cooked): 3 heaped tablespoons
Radish: 10 radishes
Spinach (cooked): 4 heaped tablespoons
Spinach (fresh): 1 cereal bowl
Spring greens (cooked): 4 heaped tablespoons
Swede (diced and cooked): 3 heaped tablespoons
Sweet potato: 1 medium
Sweetcorn (canned): 3 heaped tablespoons
Sweetcorn on the cob: 1 cob
Sweetcorn (baby): 6-8 corn
Tomato puree (concentrated): 1heaped tablespoon
Tomato: (canned) plum 2 whole – fresh, 1 medium or 7 cherry – sundried 4 pieces
Turnip (diced and cooked): 3 heaped tablespoons
Vegetable juice: 100% unsweetened - 1 small glass (150ml) of unsweetened 100% fruit and/or vegetable juice can count as a maximum of one portion.
It is recommended that we limit 100% fruit/vegetable juices and smoothies to a combined total of 150ml per day (one portion) and consume with meals to reduce the risk of tooth decay.
Vegetable smoothie: 100% unsweetened - 1 small glass (150ml) of unsweetened 100% fruit and/or vegetable smoothie can count as a maximum of one portion.
A portion of unsweetened 100% fruit and/or vegetable smoothie includes 150ml of fruit/vegetable juice; puree; edible pulp or a combination of these.
Government advice is to limit 100% fruit juices and smoothies to a combined total of 150ml per day (one portion) and consume with meals to reduce the risk of tooth decay.
Watercress: 1 cereal/dessert bowl

FRUIT

If using dried fruit it's approximately 30g in weight for adults

Apple: fresh, 1 medium apple or 4 dried rings
Apple puree: 2 heaped tablespoons
Apricots: canned, 6 halves – fresh, 3 apricots – dried 3 whole
Avocado: half an avocado
Banana: fresh, 1 medium banana
Blackberries: 1 handful (9-10 blackberries)
Blackcurrants: 4heaped tablespoons
Blueberries: 2 handfuls (4 heaped tablespoons)
Cherries: canned, 11 cherries(3 heaped tablespoons) – fresh 14 cherries – dried 1 heaped tablespoon
Clementine: 2 clementines
Cranberries: dried 1 heaped tablespoon
Currants: dried 1 heaped tablespoon
Damsons: 5-6 damsons
Dates: dried 3 dates
Fig: fresh or dried, 2 figs
Fruit smoothie: 100% unsweetened - 1 small glass (150ml) of unsweetened 100% fruit and/or vegetable smoothie can count as a maximum of one portion. A portion of unsweetened 100% fruit and/or vegetable smoothie includes 150ml of fruit/vegetable juice; puree; edible pulp or a combination of these. It is recommended that we limit 100% fruit juices and smoothies to a combined total of 150ml per day (one portion) and consume with meals to reduce the risk of tooth decay.
Fruit salad: fresh or canned, 3 heaped tablespoons
Grapefruit: canned, 3 heaped tablespoons (8 segments) – fresh ½ grapefruit
Grapes: 1 handful /14 grapes
Kiwi fruit: 2 fruits
Kumquat: 6-8 kumquats
Lychee (canned or fresh): 6 lychees
Mandarin orange: canned, 3 heaped tablespoons – fresh 1 medium orange
Mango: 2 slices fresh flesh – dried, 1 heaped tablespoon
Melon: 1 slice (2 inch/5cm slice)
Nectarine: 1 nectarine
Orange: 1 medium orange
Passion fruit: 5-6 Passion fruits
Peach: canned, 2 halves or 7 slices – fresh, 1 medium peach – dried, 2 halves
Pear: canned, 2 halves or 7 slices – fresh 1 medium pear – dried, 2 halves

Pineapple: canned, 2 rings or 12 chunks – fresh 1 large slice – dried, 2 rings or 1 heaped tablespoon
Plum: 2 medium plums
Prunes: canned, 6 prunes – ready to eat, 3 prunes – dried, 3 prunes
Raspberries: canned fresh or frozen – 20 raspberries
Raisins: 1 heaped tablespoon
Rhubarb: canned, 5 chunks – stewed, 2 heaped tablespoons
Satsuma: 2 small satsumas
Sharon fruit: 1 sharon fruit
Strawberry: canned, 9 strawberries – fresh, 7 strawberries
Sultanas: 1 heaped tablespoon
Tomato puree (concentrated): 1 heaped tablespoon
Tomato: (canned) plum 2 whole – fresh, 1 medium or 7 cherry – sundried 4 pieces

Reference NHS Choices 2019, 5ADAY Portion Guide

Try to have a rainbow of fruit and vegetables every day!

Herbs and spices are a fabulous way to make your meals pop with flavour.

Spices can be kept longer than herbs, although once opened they will deteriorate, so I recommend that you discard them after three months of opening to ensure you get the best flavour, otherwise they can start to take on a bitter flavour or even lose their flavour completely. Always keep your spices out of direct sun light and seal well after use. The strongest flavours are achieved by grinding fresh seeds or whole spices as opposed to buying them already ground.

Tip - warm your spices gently in a frying pan before grinding to release the aromatic flavours. Add at the beginning of a recipe to allow the flavour to develop during cooking.

Know your herbs and spices...
BASIL lifts any tomato-based dish, try fresh basil leaves
CARDAMOM add the seeds to rice, couscous and curries to give a sweet aromatic touch.
CARAWAY small black seeds used in cakes and great sprinkled on meat for barbecues.
CAYENNE intense heat so use sparingly. Used to dust seafood.
CHILLI use fresh for a strong zingy flavour or dried for less heat.
CINNAMON add whole quills to sauces or use a tiny amount of ground for cakes and puddings.
CORIANDER add to both sweet and savoury dishes. Use in tomato sauces or cakes for a mild spice. Perfect, fresh, ground or in seed form.
CUMIN slightly bitter. Seeds need to be fried to release the flavour. Perfect in curries or sprinkle the seeds over potatoes before roasting.
CURRY POWDER use to pep up pasta and rice or add flavour to curries and casseroles.
FENNEL SEED strong flavour of aniseed for pasta, curries and casseroles.
GARAM MASALA great base for curries. Add at the beginning and a little at the end of cooking to give two depths of flavour.
GINGER buy fresh and store in foil in the fridge. No need to peel, the skin is packed full of flavour, and if you grate it rather than chop it you will get more of that lovely natural heat. Great in curries and a great alternative to the heat from chillies if you have someone who is allergic to chilli.
PAPRIKA great smoked added to sausages for a chorizo flavour.
PARSLEY great with fish or in salads.
PEPPERCORNS perfect to bring any meal to life. Try red peppercorns for a more subtle flavour. Peppercorns are best used freshly ground.

ROSEMARY add to lamb dishes or roast potatoes. Try a sprig of fresh Rosemary in a gin & tonic!

SALT – a great way to bring out the flavour of a dish, but use sparingly as we should only have a maximum of 6g per day.

STAR ANISE use in mulled wine, beef stews or add to tomato-based sauces.

THYME works well with many meats, tomatoes and Mediterranean style recipes.

TURMERIC a great colour enhancer to curries and stews, and packed full of antioxidants too!

Exercise

Exercise is vital not just to weight loss but to our general health and wellbeing.

Here are just a few reasons why you should exercise regularly.

- Strengthens muscles
- Reduces body fat
- Releases the feel-good hormone, helping to reduce stress, anxiety and depression
- Improves energy levels
- Improves sleep quality
- Reduces the risk of developing type 2 diabetes
- Keeps your bones strong
- Helps to lower raised blood pressure levels
- Helps to reduce cholesterol levels
- Improves lung capacity
- Boosts your immune system
- Boosts memory and improves cognitive function

Don't worry; this does not mean you need to join your local gym and become a lycra gym bunny! But you do need to focus on making sure you adopt some form of activity into your lifestyle; however busy you are.

With this plan, I've kept it simple; aim for 30 minutes of walking outside every day, everything else is a bonus.

Walking is a fabulous all-rounder; it has an aerobic element (this means your heart and lungs will work a little harder than usual, thus burning fat). You'll strengthen and tone your muscles, especially your leg and stomach muscles. But just as importantly walking outside helps to clear your head, and this helps with those stress levels.

If you can't get 30 minutes in one go, then there is no need to worry. Smaller bite-size chunks spread across the day is perfectly fine too.

During the trials I conducted, everyone who managed to achieve the walking goal, not only felt better, they felt less stressed, more focused and they slept better. They lost inches too!

"I was hoping to lose weight but surprised to experience improvements in my sleep and mood. I feel energised and look forward to my daily walk even in the rain!"
- Janet M

Get walking

Wearing the correct shoes while walking is essential, so choose shoes or trainers that have excellent arch support and cushioned soles. If you are thinking about more countryside based walking then investing in a pair of walking boots would be a wise decision as they provide more support to your ankles.

Clothing, wear clothing that is slightly loose and comfortable, there's no need to invest in that lycra!

If you are going on a long walk wearing several layers is best rather than a thick top as it allows you to control your temperature more effectively.

As with all exercise, staying hydrated is vital as you will need to replace fluids lost through exertion, however large or small that may be. Water is perfect for this and if you are going for a longer walk, may over an hour then a little snack would be a good idea to take with you (see page **65** for suggestions).

If you've not walked any distance before or are recovering from illness or injury, then it's best to begin slowly and gradually. Walking with a friend is a great motivator, making it much more enjoyable and increasing your chances of keeping it up in the long term. Start by underestimating rather than overestimating your capabilities: you'll soon learn how far you can walk before you start to feel tired.

Don't push yourself too hard on distance and terrain: the idea is to enjoy yourself, and if you end up too stiff and sore, it might put you off going out again. Remember the best activity for you is one that you want to do regularly.

Don't forget, if you have any concerns about your joints (ankles, knees, back or hips), discuss your exercise plans with your doctor before embarking on a new regime.

Getting going

Walking for health

- Maintain a good posture by standing tall with arms loosely by your sides, and pull your stomach in towards your spine. Keep your shoulders back, down and relaxed.
- Make sure your heel strikes the ground first.

- Let your arms swing naturally at your sides.

Walking for Fitness

- Walk with a more determined stride, heel down first with toes high, at a faster pace – just below a jogging pace.
- Create a forceful push-off from the back foot.
- Elbows are bent at a 90-degree angle and fingers loosely curled.
- Lean slightly forward, pulling your stomach muscles in towards your spine

Weeks 1 & 2

Walk four/five times per week, starting with the health walk for a total of 5-15 minutes and gradually try to increase the duration of your walk, minute by minute, ready to go on to weeks three and four.

Weeks 3 & 4

Continue walking four/five times a week with your healthy walk. On three of those walks, start with your healthy walk pace for approx. 10 minutes then increase the speed to a fitness level for a further 5 minutes, then back to a health walk than 8-10 minutes.

Weeks 5 & 6

Increase to six to seven times per week. On four of those walks, start with your healthy walk pace for approx. 10 minutes then increase the speed to a fitness level for a further 10 minutes, then back to a health walk than 8-10 minutes.

Weeks 7 & 8

Continue walking six/seven times a week with your healthy walk. On five of those walks, start with your healthy walk pace for approx. 10 minutes then increase the speed to a fitness level for a further 10 minutes, then back to a health walk than 10 minutes.

Weeks 9 and beyond

Build up to seven times per week. You should now be capable of 30 minutes of continuous walking using the fitness walk. If time is short, this can split into two 15-minute sessions.

"This is a very easy plan to follow ! So easy to follow, doesn't feel like dieting at all , just healthy eating, with a varied diet, plus no calorie counting! Have felt really well, slept well and I can't believe that I would ever like walking so much! Fantastic results, weight loss and inches. Thank you Sarah for the Healthy Living Plan."
- Tanya D

21 day
STARTER PLAN

Welcome to my 21 day starter plan.

This three-week plan is designed to get you going in the right direction without having to overthink it.

All of the meal suggestions are interchangeable. You can add your own meal choices in by following the principles discussed earlier in the book, or any of my recipes.

I recommend that you have approximately 400ml of milk (this can be animal or plant-based) each day. This can be used in cereals and drinks. If you are choosing cows milk, then semi-skimmed milk is perfectly fine, however, if you are choosing a plant-based option, then it should contain added calcium.

To help you identifiy vegertarian or vegan choices, you will find the following key:
V - Vegetarian
VG - Vegan

Try and keep desserts to a max of 2-3 times per week if you can, and if you are going to have that sweet treat after dinner, avoid any snacks that day. You will find snack suggestions on page **65**.

As you know, walking is a vital part of your new healthier lifestyle, but you will see that I have included a bonus daily exercise challenge for the next 21 days that you might like to try – the choice is yours, but if you do, then the results will be even more impressive!

Good luck!

Breakfast

35g Shreddies served with 150ml milk and topped with 7 strawberries, sliced. **VG**

Porridge made with 30g (dry weight porridge oats) cooked with 200ml of water (or milk from your allowance) topped with 110g fresh blueberries and ½ tsp flaxseeds. **VG**

1 slice wholemeal or multigrain bread toasted and spread with a little Marmite and 3 Brazil nuts. **VG**

Lunch

Ham and egg salad made with 60g lean sliced ham, 1 hard-boiled medium egg (chopped), 2 large handfuls of salad leaves, plus 2 tomatoes, a chunk of cucumber, diced topped with 1 tbsp reduced-fat dressing.

Quick Mexican Rice and Quinoa Salad – see page **128**. **VG**

Quick and Simple Pea Soup – see page **115**. For dessert 2 tbsp of low-fat Greek yoghurt topped with 1 apple, diced. **V**

Dinner

Three Bean Enchiladas – see page **112** served with 4 tbsp mixed vegetables (not potatoes). **V**

Sweet Potato and Okra Stew – see page **125** served with (60g dry weight) basmati rice, cooked. **VG**

1 medium chicken breast, sprinkled with some mixed herbs, baked in the oven and served with 120g boiled potatoes and unlimited mixed green vegetables.

Bonus daily exercise challenge

Hold a small water bottle or 400g can of food in each hand, gently take the arms out to the side, keeping the elbows slightly bent, shoulders back and down. Raise your arms slowly (4-second count) to shoulder height and gently lower. Repeat eight times, rest, then repeat twice more if you can.

day 2

Breakfast

1 slice wholemeal/multigrain bread, toasted and served with 1 medium egg – boiled, scrambled or poached. **V**

3 tablespoons of plain yoghurt (plant-based), mixed with 1 tsp chia seeds and a small banana, peeled and sliced. **VG**

40g of any high-fibre, no-added sugar cereal, served with 150ml milk. **VG**

Lunch

1 wholemeal pitta bread filled with salad leaves, 30g reduced-fat cheddar cheese, grated and topped with 1 tsp Branston pickle or reduced-fat salad cream. Plus eight strawberries for dessert. **V**

1 slice wholemeal/multigrain bread, toasted and topped with 220g (small can) of no-added sugar baked beans. **VG**

1 serving of Baked Avocado with Salmon and Egg – see page **104**, served with a large green salad.

Dinner

Half and Half Spaghetti Bolognese – see page **76** served with unlimited cooked green vegetables.

Sweet Potato with Spicy Salsa, Chickpeas and Avocado – see page **119** served with a medium mixed green salad. Plus 2 tbsp low-fat Greek style yoghurt (plant-based) topped with 3 dried apricots, chopped. **VG**

Mushroom and Cauliflower Pasta – see recipe page **130**. For dessert Sarah's Affogato see page **167**.

Bonus daily exercise challenge

Sit on a chair, back straight and tall, and stomach muscles pulled in. Raise the right leg off the floor to hip level, (to 4-second count), lower and repeat eight times, and then repeat on the left leg. Complete the whole exercise three times.

day 3

Breakfast
Banana, strawberry and oat smoothie. Place 1 small peeled banana with 4 strawberries, 1tsp of dry porridge oats and 160ml of milk into a blender and blitz until smooth, pour into a glass and serve straight away. **VG**

2 Weetabix served with 150ml milk. **VG**

1 medium banana, peeled and mashed spread over 1 slice of wholemeal/multigrain toast sprinkled with a little cinnamon or mixed spice. **VG**

Lunch
Tuna Rice Salad – see page **105**

1 slice wholemeal/multigrain bread, toasted and topped with two eggs scrambled with a little milk and seasoned with freshly ground black pepper. **V**

1 large tortilla wrap spread with 1tbs plant-based cream cheese, topped with ½ tsp flaxseeds, a little freshly ground black pepper, and a large handful of salad leaves. Rolled up and cut in half. **VG**

Dinner
Spicy Rainbow Stir-fry – see page **131** served with a small beef steak (approx 100g raw weight), grilled.

Spicy Rainbow Stir-fry – see page **131** served with 180g slice of seitan, grilled. or fried with a little rapeseed oil. **VG**

Bow Pasta with Quorn – see recipe page **121** served with 200g cooked mixed vegetables (not including potatoes). **VG**

Bonus daily exercise challenge
Abdominal curls: Lie on your back, knees bent, and feet hip width apart. Place your hands behind your head to support the neck. Lift your head and shoulders off floor, pulling tummy in tightly as you rise. Lower again slowly, keeping tummy in. Repeat this 8 -10 times.

day 4

Breakfast
40g no-added sugar muesli served with 150ml milk and topped with 7 strawberries or 80g raspberries. **VG**

Blueberry and Lemon Bircher: Mix together 120g yogurt with 100g blueberries, 30ml of milk (from your allowance), 15g raw oat bran plus 2 drops of vanilla extract and ½ tsp of fresh lemon zest. Leave in the fridge overnight. **VG**

1 slice of wholegrain bread - toasted, topped with 100g grilled mushrooms and 1 large grilled tomato. **VG**

Lunch
1 wholegrain bread roll, filled with 60g canned tuna in brine, drained, 1 tsp of sunflower or flaxseeds mixed with 1 tsp of reduced-fat mayonnaise or salad cream.

Bean soup – 1 can any brand mixed bean soup. **VG**

Mushroom omelette made using 100g sliced mushrooms, 3 eggs, a little milk and seasoned with freshly ground black pepper. **V**

Dinner
Mushroom, Spinach and Banana Blossom Linguini – see page **134** plus 1 orange or 8 strawberries for dessert. **VG**

Easy Stuffed Mexican Eggy Peppers – see page **111** served with unlimited mixed vegetables (not including potatoes). **V**

Cheats Sausage Jambalaya – see page **71** plus 1 medium banana for dessert.

Bonus daily exercise challenge
Box press-ups: Position yourself on hands and knees, hands in line with shoulders and knees directly under hips. Pull your stomach muscles in to support your back and then bend your elbows, taking forehead towards floor. Lift again without locking elbows at the top. Complete six press-ups, rest for ten seconds and repeat twice more.

Breakfast
100g Greek style yoghurt mixed with 1 tbsp reduced-sugar muesli, ¼ tsp chia seeds and 80g raspberries or blueberries. **V**

35g porridge oats cooked with water or milk from your allowance served with 125ml of any fruit juice. **VG**

45g no-added sugar muesli served with milk from your allowance and 1 tbs raisins. **VG**

Lunch
Hummus and salad wrap – made with 1 large or 2 small soft tortilla whole-wheat wraps with 1 tbsp reduced-fat hummus and unlimited mixed salad. **VG**

Mushroom Rice – see page **156**. **VG**

1 wholegrain bread roll filled with ½ small avocado, peeled and sliced, plus 1 medium egg hard-boiled, sliced and topped with 1 tsp of mayonnaise. **V**

Dinner
2 low-fat pork sausages, grilled or baked served with 140g mashed potato and unlimited mixed vegetables.

Aubergine and Lentil Bake – see page **135** served with a large mixed green salad and a small wholegrain roll or 30g crusty bread. **V**

1 vegan peppered steak - grilled and served with 140g mashed potato made with milk from your allowance, plus a little gravy and unlimited mixed vegetables. **VG**

Bonus daily exercise challenge
Tricep dips: Start with both hands resting on edge of stairs, or a step and hips close to edge. Pull your stomach in tightly and bend the elbows, lowering hips towards floor. Push up again, with shoulders down, head up and avoid locking elbows. Do eight, then rest for 10 seconds and repeat.

day 6

Breakfast
Overnight porridge with berries – 130g plain low-fat yoghurt mixed with 20g porridge oats, left over night in the fridge and served with 80g any berries. –Tip: if this is a little thick, thin down in the morning with a little milk. **VG**

40g Bran flakes served with milk from your allowance and a small banana peeled and sliced. **VG**

2 Shredded wheat served with milk from your allowance and 125ml glass of orange juice. **VG**

Lunch
Bacon and mushroom pitta – 2 lean back bacon slices (visible fat removed before cooking) fried with 100g sliced mushrooms served in wholemeal pitta bread.

Cheesy jacket sweet potato – 160-180g sweet potato baked and topped with 25g grated reduced-fat cheddar cheese or 35g low-fat cream cheese. **V**

Lentil salad – large mixed salad topped with 80g cooked mixed lentils, 6 chopped olives, ½ tsp flax seeds sprinkled over the top with 1 tbsp of any reduced fat dressing. **VG**

Dinner
200g steamed white fish served with 130g boiled baby new potatoes (with skins) and unlimited other vegetables of your choice. For dessert, 1 medium banana.

Falafel Burgers - see page **122** , served with 150g (raw weight) baked sweet potato and one corn on the cob. **VG**

3 vegetarian Lincolnshire style sausages, grilled and served with 130g boiled new potatoes (with skins) and unlimited other vegetables. For dessert, 1 apple or pear. **V**

Bonus daily exercise challenge
Stand up and sit down six times, holding your stomach muscles in tightly. Rest for ten seconds, and then repeat.

day 1

Breakfast
35g uncooked porridge oats, cooked with water or milk from your allowance with 10 sultanas, and pinch of mixed spice or ground ginger (optional). **VG**

40g Shredded Wheat Bite Size served with milk from your allowance and 1 handful of blueberries. **VG**

2 eggs scrambled with milk from your allowance and served with 100g grilled tomatoes and unlimited grilled mushrooms. **V**

Lunch
1 wholegrain bread roll, filled with 25g reduced-fat cheddar cheese, 1 beetroot sliced with 1 teaspoon of reduced-fat mayonnaise. **V**

1 wholegrain bread roll, filled with 50g meat free chicken slices, 1 medium tomato sliced, a few lettuce leaves with 1 tsp of reduced-fat dressing. **VG**

1 x 400g can of lentil soup. **VG**

Dinner
4 large Portobello mushrooms grilled served with 130g boiled baby new potatoes (with skins) and unlimited other mixed vegetables. For dessert 120g of coconut based yogurt mixed with 7 chopped strawberries, ½ tsp flaxseeds and 3 chopped almonds. **VG**

Tomato and Basil Gnocchi – see page **114** served with unlimited mixed vegetables (not including potatoes). **VG**

Chicken Stir-fry with Rice – see page **68**.

Bonus daily exercise challenge
Walk up and down the stairs 4 times consecutively.

Congratulations
you have finished week one!

You will already be starting to feel better in yourself. Both your sleep pattern and concentration should be improving too.

This week the focus is on labels. It's good to understand how food labeling works so that you can start to make more informed choices when shopping.

Many food producers have adopted the traffic light system to help you make more informed choices about the foods you buy. This system makes it easier to choose food that is lower in total fat, saturated fat, and sugar and salt. Choose more' greens',' ambers' and fewer 'reds'.

Below is a typical label-

per serving (167g)

ENERGY	FAT	SATURATES	SUGAR	SALT
992kJ 237kcal	12g MED	7.5g HIGH	4.6g LOW	0.95g MED
12%	17%	38%	5%	16%

of your reference intake
Typical values per 100g: Energy 593kJ/141kcal

For your information
Total fat -
High: more than 17.5g of fat per 100g
Low: 3g of fat or less per 100g

Saturated fat -
High: more than 5g of saturated fat per 100g
Low: 1.5g of saturated fat or less per 100g

Sugars -
High: more than 22.5g of total sugars per 100g
Low: 5g of total sugars or less per 100g

Salt and sodium -
Salt is also called sodium chloride. Sometimes, food labels only give the figure for sodium. But there's a simple way to work out how much salt you're eating from the sodium figure: salt = sodium x 2.5.(one part of salt is equal to 2.5 parts of sodium). Adults should eat no more than 2.4g of sodium per day, as this is equal to 6g of salt.
High: more than 1.5g salt per 100g (or 0.6g sodium)
Low: 0.25g salt or less per 100g (or 0.1g sodium)

day 8

Breakfast

100g plain yoghurt mixed with 1 tbsp no-added sugar muesli, ¼ tsp chia seeds and 80g raspberries or blueberries. **VG**

1 slice of wholemeal/multigrain toast topped with 150g no-added sugar baked beans. **VG**

35g of any no-added sugar cereal served with milk from your allowance, plus 125ml fruit juice. **VG**

Lunch

Hummus and beetroot wrap – made with 1 large or 2 small soft tortilla whole wheat wraps with 1 ½ tbsp reduced-fat hummus and 100g grated beetroot. **VG**

Salmon pitta – 1 wholemeal pitta bread filled with salad and 70g canned salmon.

Egg salad – made with 2 hard-boiled eggs, large mixed salad, topped with 1 tsp mixed seeds and 1 tbsp reduced fat salad dressing. **V**

Dinner

Korean Chicken with Noodles – see page **87**, served with unlimited steamed broccoli.

1 medium meat free chicken style breast fillet, grilled, served with 130g boiled new potatoes (with skins) plus unlimited mixed vegetables and 200g mixed berries for dessert. **V**

Falafel (5 balls) served on a large mixed rainbow salad (use different coloured vegetables such as beetroot, peppers, radish etc.), sprinkled with 2 tsps sunflower seeds, ½ tsp chia seeds and drizzled with a little reduced-fat dressing of your choice and served with 30g fresh crusty bread. **VG**

Bonus daily exercise challenge

Stand up and sit down 10 times, holding your stomach muscles in tightly. Rest for ten seconds, then repeat.

day 9

Breakfast
Bacon style sandwich: 3 rashers lean bacon or vegan style bacon slices grilled, placed between 2 slices wholemeal or multigrain bread spread with a little ketchup. **VG**

1 slice of wholemeal/multigrain toast topped with a medium sized banana mashed and 3 strawberries sliced on top sprinkled with ½ tsp chia seeds. **VG**

40g no-added sugar muesli topped with 80g fresh berries or 1 chopped apple or pear and served with milk from allowance. **VG**

Lunch
1 slice of wholemeal/multigrain toast topped with Pea Puree – see page **157**. **V**

Spicy Seitan and Noodle Soup - see page **138**. **VG**

Bacon and mushroom pitta – 2 lean back bacon slices (visible fat removed before cooking) grilled with100g sliced mushrooms served in a wholemeal pitta bread.

Dinner
Quick Fish Curry – see page **108** served with cooked basmati rice (60g dry weight).

Wild Mushroom Ristto – see page **123**, served with a large green salad plus 1 apple or pear for dessert. **V**

Aubergine, Chickpea and Quorn Tagine – see page **138** served with cooked basmati rice (60g dry weight) **VG**

Bonus daily exercise challenge
Outer thigh toner: Lie on your side with your lower arm outstretched and head resting on towel. Keeping your shoulders and hips stacked on top of each other, bend bottom leg to 90 degrees. Extend top leg, with foot flexed, in line with hip. Lift leg to just above hip height, pressing leg away from you. Lower the leg and repeat 10 times. Repeat on the other side. Rest for 10 seconds and complete the whole section again.

day 10

Breakfast

2 low fat sausages (pork or plant based), grilled and served with 100g mushrooms poached in a little vegetable stock, with 3 tomatoes cut in half, grilled and 2 tablespoons of no-added sugar baked beans. **VG**

1 Weetabix served with milk from your allowance and topped with a small banana sliced. **VG**

2 crumpets toasted spread with a little marmite. **VG**

Lunch

Super Quick Sausage Bagel Pizza – see page **75**.

Cheese Quesadillas - see page **110**. **V**

Feta Style Bean Wraps - see page **129**. **VG**

Dinner

Quick Seitan Dhansak Curry – see page **137** sserved with cooked basmati rice (60g dry weight). **VG**

Cod on a Bed of Smoky Beans – see page **95** served with unlimited vegetables (not including potatoes).

Simple Quorn Korma – see page **124** served with cooked basmati rice (60g dry weight). **VG**

Bonus daily exercise challenge

Abdominal curls: Lie on your back, knees bent, and feet hip width apart. Place your hands behind your head to support the neck. Lift your head and shoulders off floor, pulling tummy in tightly as you rise. Lower again slowly, keeping tummy in. Repeat this 8 -10 times.

day 11

Breakfast
1 wholemeal bagel, cut in half and toasted, topped with a little Marmite. **VG**

80g no-added sugar baked beans, 2 tomatoes, halved and grilled, 100g mushrooms cooked in stock without fat, plus 1 slice wholemeal/multigrain toast. **VG**

35g porridge oats cooked with water or milk from your allowance served with 125ml of orange juice. **VG**

Lunch
1 medium baked potato filled with 50g canned tuna, 1 tbsp of sweetcorn with 2 tsp of reduced-fat mayonnaise or salad cream.

Tomato and Olive Pasta – see page **118**, served with either a small mixed salad or 3 tbsp mixed cooked vegetables (not including potato). **VG**

Sweet Potato Soup - see page **132**. **VG**

Dinner
1 Quorn vegan breaded fillet cooked and served with Mushroom Rice – see page **156** and a small salad. **VG**

2 Quorn Cumberland sausages cooked and served with Cauliflower Hash Browns – see page **145** and 1 corn on the cob. **V**

Rich Sausage and Mushroom Casserole – see page **74** served with 2 tbsp of mashed potato and unlimited green cooked vegetables.

Bonus daily exercise challenge
Box press-ups: Position yourself on hands and knees, hands in line with shoulders and knees directly under hips. Pull your stomach muscles in to support your back and then bend your elbows, taking forehead towards floor. Lift again without locking elbows at the top. Complete eight press-ups, rest for ten seconds and repeat twice more

day 12

Breakfast
Berry Breakfast: Place 150g of mixed berries fresh or frozen into a saucepan add ½ teaspoon of sugar and simmer for 4-5 minutes. Remove from the heat and allow to cool for 20 minutes. Serve with 100g 2% fat Greek style yoghurt and top with 2 tps of granola or muesli. **V**

1 medium egg, boiled or poached, served on 1 slice wholemeal/multigrain bread, toasted and spread with Marmite. **V**

40g muesli topped with 1 chopped apple or pear, sprinkled with ½ tsp flaxseeds and served with milk from your allowance. **VG**

Lunch
1 medium wholemeal pitta bread filled with 1 tbsp reduced fat hummus and chopped red pepper and served with a small green salad. **VG**

Pearl Couscous salad – see page **143**. **VG**

Ploughman's roll - made with 1 multigrain bread roll, filled with lettuce, a small apple, cored and sliced, 2 tsp pickle, 1 thin slice of lean ham and 25g reduced-fat cheddar cheese.

Dinner
Thai Style Fish Cakes – see page **100** served with Hassleback Baked Sweet Potato – see page **142** and unlimited green cooked vegetables.

Aubergine, Chickpea and Quorn Tagine– see page **138** served with Couscous with Fruit and Nuts – see page **144**. **VG**

Falafel Burgers – see recipe **122** served with Spicy Sweet Potato Chips – see page **153**.

Bonus daily exercise challenge
Sit on a chair, have one leg bent with the foot flat on the floor. Raise the other leg and draw the alphabet in the air with your foot. Repeat with the other leg.

day 13

Breakfast
Banana and Vanilla Bircher: Peel and finely chopped one medium banana. Mix the banana with 120g plain yoghurt, 2 drops of vanilla extract, ¼ tsp chia seeds and 15g of raw oatbran. Soak overnight in the fridge. Serve with 3 almonds roughly chopped sprinkled over the top. **VG**

45g Shreddies served with milk from your allowance. **VG**

1 slice wholemeal/multigrain toast topped with 200g cooked tinned plum tomatoes, seasoned with a little freshly ground black pepper. **VG**

Lunch
Cheese, beetroot and coleslaw roll made with 1 multigrain bread roll, 25g reduced-fat cheddar cheese, grated beetroot and 1 tbsp coleslaw. **V**

Avocado and cream cheese on rye bread. Mash the flesh from 1 small avocado with 20g low-fat cream cheese, a little black pepper and spread over two slices of rye bread. Sprinkle with ¼ teaspoon flaxseeds. **VG**

1 x medium oven-baked sweet potato topped with 100g no-added sugar baked beans and served with a mixed side salad. **VG**

Dinner
Sweet and Sour Chicken with Rice -see page **89**.

Spicy Mexican Stir-fry - made with 150g Quorn Vegan Sizzling Mexican Strips, 250g stir-fry vegetables, seasoned with a little sweet chilli sauce (optional) and fresh lime juice. **VG**

Chilli Con Carne with Rice – see page **84** – see the tip at the bottom of the recipe, to make this a vegetarian dish. **V**

Bonus daily exercise challenge
Abdominal curls: Lie on your back, knees bent, and feet hip width apart. Place your hands behind your head to support the neck. Lift your head and shoulders off floor, pulling tummy in tightly as you rise. Lower again slowly, keeping tummy in. Repeat this 12 -14 times.

day 14

Breakfast
1 egg poached, served with 1 vegetarian sausage - grilled, 80g no-added sugar baked beans, 1 tomato, cut in half - grilled, 1 large mushroom grilled, and 1 slice wholemeal/multigrain toast. **VG**

2 Quorn Vegan sausages - grilled, 80g no-added sugar baked beans, 1 tomato, cut in half - grilled, 1 large mushroom grilled, and 1 slice wholemeal/multigrain toast. **VG**

1 egg poached, served with 1 low-fat sausage - grilled, 80g no-added sugar baked beans, 1 tomato, cut in half - grilled, 1 large mushroom grilled, and 1 slice wholemeal/multigrain toast.

Lunch
Quick Naan Bread Chicken and Sweetcorn Pizza – see page **77**.

Cheesy Vegetable Pasta – see page **113**. **V**

Lentil, olive and seed salad – large mixed salad topped with 80g cooked mixed lentils, 8 black olives, sliced, 1 teaspoon mixed seeds and 1tablespoon reduced-fat dressing. **VG**

Dinner
2 vegan sausages cooked with 2 Portobello mushrooms sliced and served with Simple Vegetable Rice – see page **154**. **VG**

1 Quorn garlic and herb fillet cooked and served with Roasted Ratatouille – see page **120**.

1 skinless chicken breast cooked to your liking and served with Roasted Ratatouille – see page **120**.

Exercise challenge for the day
Walk up and down the stairs 6 times consecutively.

Congratulations
you have finished week two!

As you know, being active is the key to getting healthier. Have you increased your activity from day one? If not, then now is the time to ask yourself the question, why not? Think about the elements you can improve on. Any positive change, however significant is a step in the right direction!

Maybe plan to meet up with a friend and go for a walk with them, just getting out and meeting people can motivate you to be proactive.

The focus this week is on eating slower. Yes, it may seem a bit strange; however, there can be a delay between physically eating and your brain, recognising that the event has happened and that you are full. When we eat too quickly, we can overeat because the chemicals in our brain that make us feel full have not been activated.

So, eating slower makes a big difference.

If you think about this in a real-life scenario. When you go out for dinner with friends, you will often find that you feel full and struggle to eat the whole meal. This is not always because you've eaten more, but because you have been talking between mouthfuls and your brain is getting those signals and telling you it's time to stop. By eating slower at home, we can replicate the scenario, and we naturally consume less food, but don't feel hungry. By eating the right types of foods, we are unlikely to feel hungry a few hours later too.

day 15

Breakfast
35g Shreddies served with 150ml milk and topped with 80g raspberries. **VG**

Porridge made with 35g (dry weight porridge oats) cooked with water or milk from your allowance topped with 1 small apple chopped and ½ tsp flaxseeds. **VG**

1 slice wholemeal or multigrain bread toasted and spread with a little Marmite and 3 Brazil nuts. **VG**

Lunch
Prawn and egg salad made with 60g cooked peeled prawns, 1 hard-boiled medium egg (chopped), 2 large handfuls of salad leaves, plus 2 tomatoes, a chunk of cucumber, diced, topped with 1 tbsp reduced-fat dressing.

200g no-added sugar baked beans served on 1 slice of toasted wholemeal/multigrain bread. **VG**

Simple Vegetable Rice – see page **154**, topped with 4 slices of Quorn Vegan Chicken Free Slices, shredded and 1 apple or pear for dessert. **VG**

Dinner
Indian Style Roasted Cauliflower Steaks – see page **126**, served with Avocado Fries – see page **152**. **VG**

Tomato, Caper and Olive Tempeh – see page **140** served with cooked pasta (70g dry weight). **VG**

1 lean pork loin chop (fat removed before cooking), grilled to your liking, served with 130g mashed potatoes and unlimited mixed green vegetables.

Exercise challenge for the day
Hold a small water bottle or 400g can of food in one hand, gently pass the weight over the top of your head into the other hand and down to your side, and then bring it back. Repeat ten times.

day 16

Breakfast
1 slice wholemeal/multigrain bread, toasted and served with 1 medium egg – boiled, scrambled or poached. **V**

3 tbsp of plain yoghurt (plant-based), mixed with 1 tsp chia seeds and a small banana, peeled and sliced. **VG**

40g of any high-fibre, no-added sugar cereal, served with 150ml milk from your allowence. **VG**

Lunch
1 wholemeal pitta bread filled with mixed salad leaves, 3 slices of Quorn Vegan Chicken Free Slices, shredded topped with 1 tsp Branston pickle or reduced-fat mayonnaise. Plus eight strawberries for dessert. **VG**

1 x 400g can of any flavoured vegetable based soup. **VG**

Mushroom omelette made with 3 medium eggs, 20g reduced-fat cheese and 100g mushrooms.

Dinner
Salmon with a Warm Spinach and Chickpea Salad – see page **99**.

3 vegetarian sausages grilled and served with Roasted Ratatouille – see page **120**. **V**

Chinese Style Tempeh - see page **139** served with cooked basmati rice (60g dry weight) and 120g steamed broccoli. **VG**

Exercise challenge for the day
Sit on a chair, back straight and tall, and stomach muscles pulled in. Raise the right leg off the floor to hip level, (to 4-second count), lower and repeat ten times, then repeat on the left leg. Complete the whole exercise four times.

day 17

Breakfast

Banana, blueberry and oat smoothie. Place 1 small peeled banana with 50g fresh or frozen blueberries, 1 tsp of dry porridge oats and 160ml of milk into a blender and blitz until smooth, pour into a glass and serve straight away. **VG**

1 Weetabix served with150ml milk from your allowence and topped with 1 medium banana peeled and sliced. **VG**

1 small avocado, peeled and mashed spread over 1 slice of wholemeal/multigrain toast. **VG**

Lunch

Cheesy Vegetable Pasta – see page **113**. **V**

100g reduced fat hummus, eaten with a selection of raw vegetables and 1 pear for dessert.

1 large tortilla wrap spread with 1 tbsp plant-based cream cheese, topped with ½ a small avocado sliced, ½ tsp flaxseeds, a little freshly ground black pepper, and a large handful of salad leaves. Rolled up and cut in half. **VG**

Dinner

Cauliflower Hash Browns – see page **145** served with a Quorn Breaded Fishless Fillet, and 2 tbsp of sweetcorn or peas. **V**

Tomato and basil Gnocchi – see page **114** served with a Quorn Breaded Fishless Fillet. **VG**

Sausage Shakshuka – see page **86**.

Exercise challenge for the day

Stand up and sit down ten times, holding your stomach muscles in tightly. Rest for ten seconds, and then repeat twice more.

day 18

Breakfast
1 Oat, Banana, Apple and Walnut Cookie – see page **169** plus 7 strawberries. **V**

Blueberry and Lemon Bircher: Mix together 120g yogurt with 100g blueberries, 30ml of milk (from your allowance), 15g raw oat bran plus 2 drops of vanilla extract and ½ tsp of fresh lemon zest. Leave in the fridge over night. **VG**

Banana and Granola Stuffed Baked Apple – see page **168 VG**

Lunch
1 wholegrain bread roll, filled with 60g cooked chicken, 1 tsp of reduced-fat mayonnaise or salad cream and a small side salad.

Quick Quinoa, bulgar wheat and avocado salad – ½ pack (125g) of ready cooked, mixed with ½ small avocado, peeled, de-stoned and diced, and 1 small carrot grated – dressed with 1 tbsp reduced-fat dressing. **VG**

1 large soft tortilla wrap, filled with 25g grated reduced-fat cheese, 1 tbsp reduced-fat coleslaw and lettuce leaves. **V**

Dinner
Vegan Cheesy Cottage Pie – see page **117** served with unlimited green mixed vegetables (not including potatoes). **VG**

Vegetarian Cheesy Cottage Pie – see page **133** served with unlimited green mixed vegetables (not including potatoes). **V**

Cheesy Cottage Pie – see page **91**, served with unlimited green mixed vegetables (not including potatoes).

Exercise challenge for the day
Box press-ups: Position yourself on hands and knees, hands in line with shoulders and knees directly under hips. Pull your stomach muscles in to support your back and then bend your elbows, taking forehead towards floor. Lift again without locking elbows at the top. Complete eight press-ups, rest for ten seconds and repeat twice more.

day 19

Breakfast
1 Oat, Banana, Apple and Walnut Cookie – see page **169** plus 80g raspberries or blueberries. **V**

35g porridge oats cooked with water or milk from your allowance served with 125ml of any fruit juice. **VG**

45g no-added sugar muesli served with milk from your allowance and 1 tbs raisins or sultanas. **VG**

Lunch
King Prawn and Asparagus Linguine – see page **101**.

Quick Mexican Rice and Quinoa Salad – see page **128**. **VG**

1 wholegrain bread roll filled with salad, plus 1 medium egg hard-boiled, sliced and topped with 1 tsp of reduced-fat mayonnaise. **V**

Dinner
Chicken Stir-fry with Rice – see page **68**, 7 strawberries or 1 orange for dessert.

Aubergine and Lentil Bake – see page **135** served with a 160-180g sweet potato baked. **V**

1 vegan peppered steak - grilled and served with Spicy Sweet Potato Chips – see page **153** unlimited green vegetables. **VG**

Exercise challenge for the day
Tricep dips: Start with both hands resting on edge of stairs, or a step, and hips close to edge. Pull your stomach in tightly and bend the elbows, lowering hips towards floor. Push up again, with shoulders down, head up and avoid locking elbows. Do ten, then rest for 10 seconds and repeat twice more.

day 20

Breakfast
1 Oat, banana, apple and walnut cookie – see page **169** plus 1 pear. **V**

40g Bran flakes served with milk from your allowance and topped with 7 strawberries sliced. **VG**

35g Shreddies served with milk from your allowance and 150ml glass of orange juice. **VG**

Lunch
Quick Prawn and Courgette Rice – see page **94** 1 medium banana for dessert.

Cheese Quesadillas – see page **110**, served with a large mixed salad. **V**

1 large soft tortilla wrap, filled with 50g meat free chicken slices, 1 medium tomato chopped, lettuce leaves, cucumber with 1 tsp of reduced-fat mayonnaise or dressing. **VG**

Dinner
2 low-fat sausages, grilled with 1 medium sized jacket potato topped, with 100g no-added sugar baked beans and 50g cooked sweetcorn.

80g sliced seitan, sprinkled with seasoning of your choice, baked and served with 150g (raw weight) baked sweet potato and 50g cooked sweetcorn. **VG**

2 vegetarian Lincolnshire style sausages, grilled with 1 medium sized jacket potato topped, with 100g no-added sugar baked beans and 50g cooked sweetcorn. **V**

Exercise challenge for the day
Abdominal curls: Lie on your back, knees bent, and feet hip width apart. Place your hands behind your head to support the neck. Lift your head and shoulders off floor, pulling tummy in tightly as you rise. Lower again slowly, keeping tummy in. Complete this 10 times, rest for ten seconds and repeat.

day 21

Breakfast

35g uncooked porridge oats, cooked with water or milk from your allowance with 10 sultanas, and pinch of mixed spice or ground ginger (optional). **VG**

40g Shredded Wheat Bite Size served with milk from your allowance and 1 handful of blueberries. **VG**

1 wholemeal bagel split in half, toasted and spread with a little honey. **V**

Lunch

1 wholegrain bread roll, spread with 2 tsps low-fat cream cheese and 30g smoked salmon, plus 6 cherry tomatoes on the side.

Tomato and Olive Pasta – see page **118**, served with a large green salad. **VG**

1 medium baked sweet potato, topped with 1tbsp low-fat cream cheese and 1 tbsp sweetcorn. **V**

Dinner

Simple Quorn Korma – see page **124** served with cooked basmati rice (60g dry weight). **VG**

Aubergine, Chickpea and Quorn Tagine – see page **138** served with 1 medium baked sweet potato. **VG**

120g beef steak, grilled to your liking served with 100g grilled mushrooms, 1 corn on the cob and Spicy Sweet Potato Chips – see page **153**.

Exercise challenge for the day

Standing tall, hips tucked under, shoulders back and down. Pull your stomach muscles in and lift your right knee to hip height, lower and repeat on the left leg. Repeat these 20 times. You can use a chair or wall for support.

Congratulations
you have finished week three!

The first few weeks are the hardest, but you have done it! You will be feeling better in your general wellbeing; your vital measurements will be decreasing, and you are a massive step closer to being where you want to be.

So, what happens now?
This is all about lifestyle and not a short-term quick fix, so stopping and going back to where you were before you started is simply not an option if you want to succeed.

Continue to adopt the principles laid out on pages **13**, (you can repeat the 21 day plan if you like), and you will continue to see great results. When you get to your goal, just carry on as you have been as your body will naturally slow down the weight loss, and it will automatically go into maintenance mode without you having to do anything.

Keep your food choices varied or your body will get stuck in a rut and slow down. Limit things like cake and meals out to once a week, and if you do have something that's beyond the normal, just walk a little bit extra the next day. TIP – DO NOT try and starve yourself the next day – it really won't work! Pick up from where you left off, don't worry about it and realise it's all part of life. No-one is perfect, there are always bumps in the journey, but you can do it!

Use any of the recipes in this book, mix and match the meal suggestions, visit www.healthylivingwithsarah.com for more recipes or using the things you have learned adapt your existing recipes to make them healthier. Everything can be tweaked to make it that little bit better for you, your family and friends.

You must keep up with your walking, and it goes without saying that you can re-do the bonus exercises at any time!

> "Easy to follow plan using ordinary ingredients, no gimmicks. Solid advice for making small changes in your life which make a big difference. I've lost weight and inches and feel much more alert. This is a workable plan you can stick to!
> - Glenys B

Snacks

It's fine to have the occasional snack between meals if you feel hungry. You should not have more than 1-2 snacks per day

1 medium boiled egg
7 Olives
6 Almonds
3 Brazil nuts
4 Walnut halves
1 Cocoa and Raisin Energy ball – see page **172**
1 Date and Nut Energy ball – see page **166**
1 Ryvita high protein crisp bread spread with 1 tsp low-fat cream cheese
1 handful any raw vegetables.

1 portion Kale crisps - *Place 60g of kale leaves in a large bowl, tearing any large leaves into smaller pieces. Spray over some rapeseed oil, then rub it into the kale leaves until evenly coated. Sprinkle over 1 tsp ground cumin and mix well. Place the leaves onto the tray making sure they are not stuck to each other. Bake in a hot oven for 8-10 minutes or until crisp but still green, then leave to cool for a few mins.*
***TIP**: swap the cumin for chili powder for a different spicier flavour*

1 portion Sweet Potato crisps – *Wash 1 medium sweet potato, and pat dry – do not peel. Pre-heat the oven to 210C, 415F, Gas mark 7. Slice into very fine slices using a vegetable peeler or mandolin onto kitchen paper to absorb any moisture. Cover with kitchen paper and pat well. Lay out in a single layer on a non-stick baking tray. Season with a pinch of salt and lightly spray with oil spray. Bake in the oven for 8-10 minutes until crisp. Remove from the oven and cool on a wire rack. When cold place in bowls and serve.*

½ a small avocado
20g reduced fat cheddar
2 tsp hummus with raw vegetables
4 strawberries
1 small apple
1 small pear
3 dried apricots
3 medjool dates
Overnight Slow-roasted tomatoes – 8 pieces - See page **155**
1 handful of raw vegetables, plus 1 tbsp salsa
2 Courgette Bombs - See page **146**
1 stick of celery filled with 2 tsp of peanut or almond butter

“I have found the eating plan easy to follow and the meals very filling. It has stopped me snacking as I am full until next meal time. I have been sleeping better and my head feels less foggy.**”**
- Julie C

“I am really enjoying real, fresh food and a focus on my wellbeing. It's a way of life I would like to adopt for life.**”**
- Gita P

“A plan that's simple, effective and delicious. Regular exercise combined with healthy eating means I have been sleeping better and generally feel more alert and ready for the day ahead. Tasty, quick, easy = 3 great words for a busy healthier lifestyle.**”**
- Ronda L

Meat

Chicken Stir-fry with Rice

Kcal	Fat	Saturates	Carbs	Sugars	Protein	Fibre	Salt
470	5.6g	1.1g	60.9g	12.3g	44.9g	5.3g	0.8g

Serves: 1   **Prep time:** 10 minutes   **Cooking time:** 15 minutes

Ingredients:
- 1x150g skinless chicken breast, sliced
- 60g basmati rice, dry weight
- 1 small red pepper, deseeded and sliced
- ½ small red chilli, sliced
- 1 spring onion, cleaned, root removed and sliced
- 40g French beans, trimmed and cut in half
- 40g mange tout
- 1 tsp honey
- 1 tsp soy sauce
- ½ tsp sesame oil
- Sesame seeds to garnish - optional

Instructions:
Bring a pan of water to the boil and add the rice.

Place the chicken slices in a bowl, and add the honey and soy sauce, stir to combine, and set aside for 5 minutes.

Heat a frying pan and add the sesame oil. Add the marinated chicken and any juices and cook for 5-6 minutes or until the chicken has browned on all sides.

Add the red pepper and cook for a further minute before adding the sliced red chilli, spring onion, french beans and mange tout, cook for a further 2-3 minutes, stirring occasionally.

Drain the rice and place in a warmed pasta bowl. Pour the chicken vegetable mix over the rice and sprinkle with the sesame seeds if using. Serve straight away.

Smoky, Spicy, Sesame Chicken

Kcal	Fat	Saturates	Carbs	Sugars	Protein	Fibre	Salt
204	7.7g	1.4g	0.7g	0.7g	37.1g	2.8g	0.54g

Serves: 1   **Prep time:** 10 minutes   **Marinating time:** 1-2 hours
Cooking time: 15 minutes

Ingredients:
- 1x150g medium skinless chicken fillet
- 1 tsp smoked paprika
- ½ tsp dried chilli flakes
- 1 tsp sesame oil

Instructions:
Place the paprika, chilli flakes and sesame oil into a small bowl and mix to make a marinade.

Brush the marinade over the chicken breast, covering it completely and place the chicken in a non-metallic oven proof dish. Cover in clingfilm and refrigerate for 1-2 hours or overnight.

Remove from the fridge and discard the clingfilm, and place on a baking tray. Preheat the oven to 180C, 350F, Gas Mark 4.

Bake in the oven, cook for 25 minutes or until the chicken is cooked through.

Serve hot or cold.

Leftover Chilli Con Carne Soup

Kcal	Fat	Saturates	Carbs	Sugars	Protein	Fibre	Salt
159	3.8g	1.5g	17.2g	11.4g	15.7g	6.9g	1.3.g

Serves: 1   **Prep time:** 2 minutes   **Cooking time:** 5-10 minutes

Ingredients:
- 200g left over chilli con carne
- 150ml tomato passata
- 100ml vegetable or beef stock
- 1tsp tomato puree

Instructions:
Place all of the ingredients into a saucepan.

Gently bring to the boil, stirring occasionally. Once the soup has come to the boil, reduce the heat to a simmer and cook for a further 5 minutes.

Season with the black pepper and serve in a warmed bowl.

Cheats Sausage Jambalaya

Kcal	Fat	Saturates	Carbs	Sugars	Protein	Fibre	Salt
398	12.4g	4.1g	48.4g	9.3g	20.7g	6.8g	1.3g

Serves: 2   **Prep time:** 5 minutes   **Cooking time:** 10 minutes

Ingredients:
- 1x250g packet of ready cooked Mexican style rice
- 1 small red pepper, deseeded and diced
- 1 small onion, peeled and finely diced
- 3 reduced fat sausages, each cut into 6 pieces
- Black pepper to season
- Rapeseed oil spray
- Fresh parsley to garnish - optional

Instructions:
Heat a frying pan and add a couple of sprays of rapeseed oil. Add the onion, red pepper and sausage pieces and cook for 4-5 minutes, stirring occasionally.

Add the rice to the frying pan with 3 tablespoons of water and cook for a further 3-4 minutes, stirring occasionally.

Remove from the heat and serve straight away with a little fresh parsley.

TIPS
- This is just as good served cold in a packed lunch
- Use vegetarian sausages to make it veggie friendly!

Rich Chicken Chasseur

Kcal	Fat	Saturates	Carbs	Sugars	Protein	Fibre	Salt
266	3.6g	0.6g	6.1g	3.2g	38.3g	1.7g	0.63g

Serves: 1   **Prep time:** 10 minutes   **Cooking time:** 25 minutes

Ingredients:
- 1x150g skinless and boneless chicken breast
- 170ml beef stock
- 80g baby button mushrooms, cleaned and cut in half
- 1 small onion, peeled and chopped
- 1 tsp tomato puree
- 30ml Brandy
- ½ tsp dried tarragon
- ½ tsp garlic paste or 1 small glove of garlic peeled and diced
- Rapeseed oil spray
- Freshly ground black pepper

Instructions:
Heat a small frying pan over medium heat. Add a couple of sprays of rapeseed oil then add garlic paste, chopped onion and mushrooms. Fry for 2-3 minutes then add the chicken breast and cook on each side until starting to brown.

Add the brandy to the pan and stir so that all of the contents are coated and then stir in the tomato puree and dried tarragon. Add the beef stock and stir to combine all of the flavours.

Reduce the heat to a simmer, and allow to cook for a further 15-20 - if the sauce gets a little too thick, thin down with a little water.

Season with a little black pepper.

Leftover Chicken and Noodle Soup

Kcal	Fat	Saturates	Carbs	Sugars	Protein	Fibre	Salt
231	3.2g	0.7g	17.8g	12g	51.7g	9.6g	1.6g

Serves: 1   **Prep time:** 5 minutes **Cooking time:** 15 minutes

Ingredients:
- 100g cooked leftover chicken, diced
- 250 ml chicken stock
- 50g cooked leftover potatoes, diced
- 50g cooked leftover carrots
- 10g dry spaghetti
- Black pepper
- A little fresh parsley for garnish (optional)

Instructions:
Place the stock into a saucepan and bring to the boil. Break the spaghetti pasta into 2cm lengths and add to the boiling stock. Reduce the heat slightly and cook for 10 mins.

Add the diced chicken, potatoes and carrots to the stock and pasta. Reduce the heat to a simmer and cook for a further 4-5 minutes.

Season with a little freshly ground black pepper and fresh parsley (if using) and serve straight away.

Rich Sausage and Mushroom Casserole

Kcal	Fat	Saturates	Carbs	Sugars	Protein	Fibre	Salt
291	21.1g	4.3g	11.7g	5.2g	24.2g	3.3g	2g

Serves: 3   **Prep time:** 5 minutes **Cooking time:** 40-45 minutes

Ingredients:
- 6 reduced fat pork sausages
- 200g tomato passata
- 150g Chestnut mushrooms, wiped and sliced
- 1 red onion peeled and diced
- 150ml full bodied red wine such as a Malbec
- 150ml beef stock
- 1 tsp smoked paprika
- 1 garlic clove, peeled and finely diced
- 1 tsp fresh thyme
- Salt and fresh ground black pepper
- Rapeseed oil spray

Instructions:
Heat a large heavy-based pan and add a couple of sprays of rapeseed oil.

Add the diced onion and garlic and cook gently for 3-4 minutes.

Add the sausages and cook for 4-6 minutes until browned.

Add the sliced mushrooms, smoked paprika and red wine, stir gently then add the tomato passata and fresh thyme.

Stir in the beef stock and reduce the heat to a simmer. Cook for 30-35 minutes.

Season with a little salt and black pepper, then sprinkle over a little fresh parsley and serve straight away.

Super Quick Sausage Bagel Pizza

Kcal	Fat	Saturates	Carbs	Sugars	Protein	Fibre	Salt
423	8.1g	2.7g	55.5g	4.8g	34.9g	4.8g	2.9g

Serves: 1   **Prep time:** 5 minutes   **Cooking time:** 10-12 minutes

Ingredients:
- 1 wholemeal bagel
- 1 reduced fat sausage
- 30g low-fat cheese, grated
- 1 tbsp tomato puree
- ½ tsp mixed dried herbs

Instructions:
Preheat the oven to 200C, 400F, Gas Mark 6

Cut the bagel in half and place onto a non-stick baking tray, cut side up.

Place the tomato puree, mixed herbs and 1tsp water into a bowl and mix until combined. Divide the tomato mixture in two and spread over the top of the cut side.

Sprinkle the grated cheese over the two bagels.

Gently run a sharp knife down the length of the sausage, just to pierce the skin. Pull the skin away and discard.   Crumble the sausage meat equally over the bagels.

Place in the oven and cook for 10 -12 minutes until the sausage has started to go golden brown.

Eat hot or cold.

Half and Half Spaghetti Bolognese

Kcal	Fat	Saturates	Carbs	Sugars	Protein	Fibre	Salt
391	4.4g	1.3g	62.8g	12.7g	26.4g	3.2g	0.74g

Serves: 2   **Prep time:** 5 minutes   **Cooking time:** 35 minutes

Ingredients:
- 100g fresh beef mince
- 50g dried red split lentils
- 100g dried spaghetti
- 1x400g can chopped tomatoes
- 1 small onion finely diced
- 1 clove of garlic, peeled and finely chopped
- 120ml water
- 3 tsp tomato puree
- 1 beef stock cube
- 1 ½ tsp dried Italian mixed herbs
- Black pepper to taste
- Fresh basil leaves to serve (optional)
- Rapeseed oil spray

Instructions:
Heat a saucepan and then add a couple sprays of the oil and add the onions and garlic, cook gently until softened.

Turn up the heat slightly and add the beef and lentils a bit at a time (this will help to stop the temperature of the pan cooling and stop the mince from boiling rather than frying) and cook until the meat has browned.

Add the tomatoes, tomato puree, water, herbs and stock cube to the mince and lentil mix and stir until all the ingredients have combined.

Reduce the heat and allow to simmer until the tomatoes and lentils have softened and the sauce has reduced – this will take about 25 minutes.

15 minutes before the Bolognese has finished cooking, bring to the boil some water in a separate saucepan and cook the spaghetti.

Season the Bolognese sauce with a little black pepper if required.

Drain the pasta and serve on warmed plates or pasta bowls, top with the Bolognese sauce.

76

Quick Naan Bread Chicken and Sweetcorn Pizza

Kcal	Fat	Saturates	Carbs	Sugars	Protein	Fibre	Salt
300	10.3g	4.1g	27.7g	4.1g	24.5g	2.5g	0.95g

Serves: 1   **Prep time:** 5 minutes   **Cooking time:** 10-12 minutes

Ingredients:
- 1 mini naan bread,
- 40g cooked chicken, diced
- 1 tbsp frozen sweetcorn
- 1 tbsp tomato puree
- ½ tsp dried mixed herbs
- 25g reduced-fat cheddar cheese, finely grated
- Black pepper

Instructions:
Pre-heat the oven to 190C, 375F, Gas Mark 5.

Place the naan bread on to a non-stick baking tray.

Spread the tomato puree over the naan bread and sprinkle over the sweetcorn and then the mixed herbs.

Top with the diced meat and then sprinkle over the grated cheese.

Place in the oven for 10-12 minutes or until the cheese is starting to colour.

Serve hot or cold.

TIP
Swap the meat and sweetcorn for toppings of your choice.

Simple Chicken Korma

Kcal	Fat	Saturates	Carbs	Sugars	Protein	Fibre	Salt
206	2.8g	0.6g	16g	6.4g	29.7g	1.2g	0.48g

Serves: 4   **Prep time:** 5 minutes   **Cooking time:** 30 minutes

Ingredients:
- 450g diced chicken breast
- 1x400ml can of coconut milk
- 1 medium onion, peeled and finely diced onion
- 30g plain flour (00 grade is best)
- 2 tbsps garam masala
- 1½ tsps turmeric
- 2 cm cube of fresh ginger peeled and finely chopped or grated
- 2 cloves of garlic peeled and finely chopped
- 2 tbsps fresh coriander roughly chopped
- 100ml water or milk
- Rapeseed oil spray

Instructions:
Add the flour and the chicken cubes to a medium sized bowl and stir until the chicken is evenly coated in the flour.

Heat a deep frying pan and add a couple of sprays of the rapeseed oil, onion and garlic and cook until soft.

Add the garam masala, ginger and turmeric to the onion/garlic mixture, stir and cook for 1 minute. Now add the chicken and flour and stir to evenly coat with the spice mixture. Continue cooking until the chicken has been sealed and is starting to take on the colour of the spices.

Gently add the coconut milk and the water or milk. Gently bring to the boil, stirring all the time to ensure the sauce does not split, reduce to a simmer and cook for a further 15 – 20 minutes until the sauce has thickened and the chicken is cooked.

Just before serving stir in the fresh coriander. Wonderful served with rice, naan or with a jacket potato.

Meatloaf Stuffed with Eggs

Kcal	Fat	Saturates	Carbs	Sugars	Protein	Fibre	Salt
431	7g	2.1g	60.9g	9g	32.2g	4.6g	2.1g

Serves: 6   **Prep time:** 10-15 minutes   **Cooking time:** 45-50 minutes

Ingredients:
- 300g lean beef mince
- 550g lean turkey mince
- 4 slices of smoked streaky bacon, finely chopped/diced
- 2 medium eggs, lightly beaten
- 4 medium eggs, hard boiled and shells removed
- 2 slices of stale bread, made into breadcrumbs
- 1 large onion, peeled and finely diced
- 2 tbsp's Worcestershire sauce
- Pinch sea salt and ½ tsp freshly ground black pepper

Instructions:
Preheat oven to 200C, 400F, Gas Mark 6

Line a 2lb loaf tin with baking parchment.

Place the beef, turkey, bacon, onion, breadcrumbs, Worcestershire sauce, salt and pepper and beaten eggs in a large mixing bowl and mix well – you may need to use your hands!

Place half the meatloaf mixture into the loaf tin and take the eggs and place them on top of the center of the meatloaf mixture.

Gently place the rest of the meatloaf mixture on top and around the eggs. Using your hands smooth the top until level.

Place in the center of the oven and bake for 45- 50 minutes, or until juices run clear. The remove from the oven and allow to rest for 5 minutes.

Remove the baking parchment and serve sliced hot or cold.

Orange & Pineapple Glazed Gammon

Kcal	Fat	Saturates	Carbs	Sugars	Protein	Fibre	Salt
332	14g	4.7g	17.8g	17.8g	33.3g	0.2g	4.3g

Serves: 6-8   **Prep time:** 20 minutes   **Cooking time:** 2-3 hours

Ingredients:
- 1.5kg boned gammon joint (unsmoked)
- 1x430g can of pineapple slices in pineapple juice
- Zest and juice of 2 large oranges
- 50g soft brown sugar
- 3 tbsps honey
- 2 tsps wholegrain mustard
- 14 cloves
- 2 bay leaves
- 1 tsp whole black peppercorns

Instructions:
Place the gammon, bay leaves and black peppercorns into a large pan. Add water, just enough to cover the gammon. Bring to the boil and allow to cook for two minutes then reduce the heat to a simmer and cook for a further hour. You may need to add more boiling water if the water level drops too low).

Drain the pineapple slices reserving the juice in a separate bowl. Arrange the pineapple slices in the bottom of a baking tray so they are roughly the same shape as the gammon joint - it's fine if they overlap.

Preheat the oven to 180C, 350F, Gas Mark 4.

Place the gammon on top of the pineapple slices and carefully remove and discard the skin, leaving behind a thin layer of fat. Using the tip of a sharp knife, score the gammon in a diamond pattern then stud the centre of each diamond with a clove.

To the bowl that has the remining pineapple juice add the orange juice and zest, honey, wholegrain mustard and brown sugar. Mix until evenly combined, then spoon the mixture over the gammon.

Roast the gammon and pineapple in the oven for 30 - 40 minutes (until cooked), ensuring you baste the gammon regularly with the juices so that you get a lovely golden brown glaze.

Remove the gammon from the oven and allow to rest for 5-10 minutes before carving. Serve hot or cold.

Lamb Kofta

Kcal	Fat	Saturates	Carbs	Sugars	Protein	Fibre	Salt
223	13g	5g	0.6g	0.1g	27.1g	0.5g	1.2g

Serves: 2 **Prep time:** 5 minutes **Cooking time:** 20 minutes

Ingredients:
- 240g lean lamb mince
- 1 ½ tsp ground cumin
- 2 tbs fresh coriander leaves, finely chopped
- 2 cloves of garlic, peeled and finely chopped
- ¼ tsp dried chilli flakes
- Pinch of salt
- Pinch of black pepper

Instructions:
Place all of the ingredients into a non-metallic bowl and mix together so everything is evenly combined.

Divide into 6 portions and shape into a sausage shape.

Heat a frying to hot and add the koftas. Cook for 4-5 minutes on each side.

Serve hot or cold. These are great served with a light herby salad and flatbreads.

Korean Beef with Noodles

Kcal	Fat	Saturates	Carbs	Sugars	Protein	Fibre	Salt
431	7g	2.1g	60.9g	9g	32.2g	4.6g	2.1g

Serves: 1   **Prep time:** 5 minutes   **Cooking time:** 10 minutes

Ingredients:
- 100g rump steak cut into strips
- 150g fresh/ready to use egg noodles
- 1 small green pepper, deseeded and sliced
- 1 spring onion, cleaned and thinly sliced
- 1 tsp grated fresh ginger
- 2 tsp soy sauce
- 1 small garlic clove, peeled and diced
- ½ tsp brown sugar
- Juice and zest of 1 lime
- Rapeseed oil spray

Instructions:
Place the beef in a bowl with the ginger, sugar, soy sauce, spring onions and lime, stir to combine coating the beef in the sauce and leave to marinate for 10 minutes.

Preheat a frying pan, add a spray of rapeseed oil and stir fry the pepper and garlic for 3-4 minutes.

Add beef and marinade sauce to the pan and cook for a further 2-3 minutes.

Add the noodles, stir and cook for another 2-3 minutes until heated through.

Serve straight away on a warmed plate.

Simple Pork and Apple Stir-fry

Kcal	Fat	Saturates	Carbs	Sugars	Protein	Fibre	Salt
364	16.6g	3.9g	19.8g	17.7g	31.5g	6.4g	0.96g

Serves: 1   **Prep time:** 15 minutes   **Cooking time:** 10-15 minutes

Ingredients:
- 120g pork loin steak, visible fat removed and cut into strips
- 200g fresh vegetable stir-fry mix
- 2 spring onions, cleaned and sliced
- 1 small apple, grated (with skin, but discard the core)
- 1 tsp fresh ginger
- 1 tsp soy sauce
- 1 tsp sesame oil
- Juice and zest of 1 lime

Instructions:
Place the pork in a bowl with the soy sauce, spring onions, ginger, sesame oil and lime, stir to combine coating the pork in the sauce and leave to marinate for 10 minutes.

Preheat a frying pan and stir fry the pork and marinade for 4-5 minutes, then add vegetables and grated apple and cook for a further 3-4 minutes. Serve straight away.

Smoky Bean & Sausage Stew

Kcal	Fat	Saturates	Carbs	Sugars	Protein	Fibre	Salt
494	12.6g	3.6g	51.9g	14.1g	38.7g	20g	1.5g

Serves: 2   **Prep time:** 5 minutes   **Cooking time:** 20 minutes

Ingredients:
- 1 small red onion, peeled and finely diced
- 1x400g can of chopped tomatoes
- 1x210g can of butter beans, drained
- 1x400g can or borlotti beans, drained
- 1x210g can of chickpeas, drained
- 3 reduced-fat pork sausages, each one cut into 4 pieces
- 1 clove of garlic, peeled and finely diced
- 2 tsps smoked paprika
- Black pepper
- Rapeseed oil spray

Instructions:
Heat a small a medium saucepan and add a couple of sprays of the rapeseed oil and add the sausages and onions and cook for 2-3 minutes, then add the garlic and cook for a further 1-2 minutes.

Add the tomatoes, paprika, butter beans, and black pepper and bring to a simmer. Cook for 10-15 mins or until slightly reduced and thickened. Season with a little black pepper and serve straight away.

Chilli Con Carne with Rice

Kcal	Fat	Saturates	Carbs	Sugars	Protein	Fibre	Salt
516	7.5g	3.2g	76.9g	14.3g	37.2g	10.3g	0.92g

Serves: 2   **Prep time:** 15 minutes   **Cooking time:** 10-12 minutes

Ingredients:
- 200g lean minced beef
- 1x400g can chopped tomatoes
- 1x210g can red kidney beans, drained and rinsed
- 120g basmati rice (dry weight)
- 1 small red onion peeled, and sliced
- 1 red pepper, deseeded and sliced
- 1 small clove of garlic, peeled and diced
- 3 tsp tomato puree
- 1 ½ tsp chilli powder
- 1 tsp cocoa powder (optional)
- Rapeseed oil spray

Instructions:
Heat a saucepan and add a couple of sprays of rapeseed oil, fry the garlic, pepper and onion for 2-3 minutes.

Add the mince beef and cook until browned (add a little at a time so the pan does not lose temperature and the meat caramelises properly).

Add the tomatoes, tomato puree, kidney beans, cocoa powder if using and chilli powder. Stir and cook over a low heat for 15-20 minutes or until the sauce is thicker.

In the meantime, bring a pan of water to the boil and cook the rice.

Drain the rice and divide between two warmed bowls, top with the chilli and serve straight away.

TIPS
• Swap the cocoa powder for a 2cm square piece of dark chocolate – adding dark chocolate makes the chilli richer in flavour
• Swap the beef mince for 200g Quorn mince to make this a vegetarian version

Left Over Chilli Pasta Bake

Kcal	Fat	Saturates	Carbs	Sugars	Protein	Fibre	Salt
520	17g	8.1g	58.6g	10.3g	33.1g	9g	1.1g

Serves: 2   **Prep time:** 15 minutes   **Cooking time:** 25 minutes

Ingredients:
• 150g dry weight pasta shapes
• 220g left over chilli con carne
• 100g low-fat cream cheese
• 75ml semi skimmed milk
• 50g reduced-fat grated cheese

Instructions:
Heat a large pan of water, and once boiling add the dry pasta and cook for 10-15 minutes (the pasta should still be slightly firm, not soft). Drain and place in a large bowl.

Preheat the oven to 190C, 375F, Gas Mark 5.

Add the left-over chilli con carne to the cooked pasta and stir to evenly combine. Then place the mixture into an oven proof dish.

Place the cream cheese and milk into a blender and blend until smooth.

Pour the cream cheese sauce over the pasta and chilli mix. Sprinkle over the grated cheese and place in the oven.

Bake for 25 minutes or until the cheese is bubbling.

Serve straight away.

Sausage Shakshuka

Kcal	Fat	Saturates	Carbs	Sugars	Protein	Fibre	Salt
550	20g	4.5g	44g	22g	53.2g	9.4g	3.2g

Serves: 1   **Prep time:** 5 minutes   **Cooking time:** 25-30 minutes

Ingredients:
- 3 chicken chipolata sausages, each cut into 3 pieces
- 1x200g can of chopped tomatoes
- 1 small egg
- 3 spring onions, cleaned and sliced
- 1 small red onion peeled and sliced
- 1 small red pepper, deseeded and diced
- 1 small orange pepper, deseeded and diced
- 1 small clove of garlic, peeled and finely diced
- ½ tsp smoked paprika
- ½ tsp cumin seeds
- Pinch cayenne pepper
- 1 tsp tomato puree
- 50ml vegetable stock
- 1 tbsp of fresh coriander leaves
- Salt and fresh ground black pepper
- Rapeseed oil spray

Instructions:
Heat frying pan and spray with a little rapeseed oil. Add the spring onions, peppers and sausages. Cook until the sausages are starting to take on a little bit of colour and the peppers and onions have started to soften.

Add the garlic and cook for a further 2 minutes, then add the cumin seeds and the paprika and cayenne into the frying pan. Stir in the tomato puree and cook for 3-4 minutes. Add the chopped tomatoes and the vegetable stock.

Reduce the heat to a simmer and cook for a further 5-10 minutes until the sauce has thickened but is not dry, then stir in the chopped coriander and season with the salt and black pepper.

Make two small wells in the tomato mixture and crack an egg into each well. If you have a lid for the frying pan place it on top, if not then take a large piece of foil and place it shiny side down gently on the top of the frying pan taking care not to touch the eggs. Cook for 3-4 minutes. Remove the lid or foil and serve straight away.

Garnish with fresh coriander or parsley leaves

Korean Chicken with Noodles

Kcal	Fat	Saturates	Carbs	Sugars	Protein	Fibre	Salt
440	4.3g	0.8g	60.1g	8.1g	41.1g	4.6g	1.5g

Serves: 1   **Prep time:** 10 minutes   **Cooking time:** 15-20 minutes

Ingredients:
• 130g skinless chicken breast cut into strips
• 150g fresh/ready to use egg noodles
• 1 small green pepper, deseeded and sliced
• 1 spring onion, cleaned and thinly sliced
• 1 tsp grated fresh ginger
• 1 tsp soy sauce
• 1 small garlic clove, peeled and diced
• ½ tsp brown sugar
• Juice and zest of 1 lime
• Rapeseed oil spray

Instructions:
Place the chicken in a bowl with the ginger, sugar, soy sauce, spring onions and lime, stir to combine coating the chicken in the sauce and leave to marinate for 10 minutes.

Preheat a frying pan, add a spray of rapeseed oil and stir-fry the pepper and garlic for 3-4 minutes.

Add chicken and marinade sauce to the pan and cook for a further 5-10 minutes, until the chicken is cooked through.

Add the noodles, stir and cook for another 2-3 minutes until heated through.

Serve straight away on a warmed plate.

Lemon Chicken with Fine Green Beans

Kcal	Fat	Saturates	Carbs	Sugars	Protein	Fibre	Salt
550	20g	4.5g	44g	22g	53.2g	9.4g	3.2g

Serves: 4   **Prep time:** 5 minutes   **Cooking time:** 25-30 minutes

Ingredients:
- 4x150g skinless chicken fillets
- 800g frozen fine green beans
- 2 lemons
- 2 tsp honey
- Salt and freshly ground black pepper
- A little fresh parsley for garnish

Instructions:
Preheat the oven to 170C, gas mark 4

Add the juice of one lemon and honey to a bowl and mix well.

Use a large ovenproof dish or deep baking tray, and line it with the frozen fine green beans.

Place the chicken breasts on top of the fine green beans and brush each chicken fillet with the lemon and honey marinade, drizzling over the remaining marinade.

Season with the salt and black pepper. Slice the remaining lemon and scatter over the lemon slices and cover the dish with foil, shiny side down. Place in the oven and bake for 30 minutes.

Increase the oven temperature to 180C, gas mark 6. Remove the foil from the dish and return the chicken to the oven for a further 5-10 minutes until golden brown on top.

Sweet and Sour Chicken with Rice

Kcal	Fat	Saturates	Carbs	Sugars	Protein	Fibre	Salt
431	2.1g	0.5g	78.8g	20.9g	34.4g	0.8g	1.4g

Serves: 2   **Prep time:** 5 minutes   **Cooking time:** 20 minutes

Ingredients:
- 2 small chicken breasts, skin removed and cut into chunks
- 120g basmati rice
- 1x200g can of pineapple chunks in juice
- 1 medium onion, peeled and diced
- 2 tbsp balsamic vinegar
- 2 tsp soy sauce
- 2 tsp dark brown sugar
- 2 tsp tomato ketchup
- 2 ½ tsp cornflour or 00 grade plain flour
- Rapeseed oil spray

Instructions:
Bring a saucepan of water to the boil and add the basmati rice.

Heat a frying pan until hot and add a couple of sprays of the oil and add the onion and chicken. Cook for 5 minutes.

In a jug add the balsamic vinegar, soy sauce, sugar, ketchup, the juice from canned pineapple and cornflour and whisk until smooth.

Add the pineapple chunks to the chicken and stir. Pour in the sweet and sour sauce and gently bring to the boil, stirring all the time. Reduce the heat to a simmer and cook for a further 1-2 minutes.

Drain the rice and dived between two warmed plates. Pour over the sweet and sour chicken and serve straight away.

Rich Beef Casserole

Kcal	Fat	Saturates	Carbs	Sugars	Protein	Fibre	Salt
389	15.7g	6.8g	22.4g	11.6g	26.4g	6.3g	1.5g

Serves: 1   **Prep time:** 10 minutes   **Marinating time:** 30 minutes
Cooking time: 60 minutes

Ingredients:
- 120g chuck steak, cut into 2cm cubes
- 200ml beef stock
- 80ml red wine
- 1 bouquet garni
- A pinch of black pepper
- 1tsp tomato puree
- 1 small garlic clove, crushed
- 1 carrot
- 1 small onion, peeled and diced
- 1 ½ tsp plain flour

Instructions:
Place the meat, red wine, bouquet garni, black pepper and garlic into a non-metallic bowl. Cover with cling film and leave to marinate for 30 minutes.

Remove the crushed garlic clove and bouquet garni from the marinade and discard. Drain the beef from the marinade ensuring you keep the marinade in a jug to use later.

Toss the beef cubes in the plain flour until evenly coated.

Preheat the oven to 160C.

Heat a non-stick saucepan and gently fry the beef and cook until brown on the outsides. Now add the onions, carrots and cook for a further 2 minutes.

Slowly add the beef stock, tomato puree and the marinade liquor, stir and bring to the boil. Turn the heat off and transfer carefully to a small ovenproof casserole dish. Cook for 1 hour until the meat is tender.

Serve hot.

Cheesy Cottage Pie

Kcal	Fat	Saturates	Carbs	Sugars	Protein	Fibre	Salt
439	9.7g	5.1g	56.2g	20.8g	32.5g	8.7g	1.7g

Serves: 1   **Prep time:** 5 minutes   **Cooking time:** 45-50 minutes

Ingredients:
- 100g lean beef mince
- 1 small red onion, peeled and finely diced
- 1 medium carrot, peeled and grated
- 100g of sweet potato, peeled and cut into small chunks
- 100g white potato, peeled and cut into small chunks
- 150ml beef stock
- 20g reduced-fat cheddar cheese
- 1 tsp tomato puree
- ½ tsp Worcestershire sauce
- Salt and black pepper

Instructions:
Preheat the oven to 200C, 400F, Gas Mark 6.

Boil the potatoes together in a saucepan of water until soft.

Heat a frying pan and add the beef mince and fry until it starts to go brown. Add the onions and grated carrot and continue to cook for a further 2-3 minutes.

Add the stock, tomato puree and Worcestershire sauce to the beef mixture, stir and reduce the heat slightly.

Drain the potatoes and mash well, seasoning with salt and black pepper. Stir in the grated cheese.

Transfer the beef mince mixture to a small ovenproof dish and spread the mashed cheesy potato over the top.

Bake in the oven for 20 minutes, or until the top has started to go brown.

Sticky Chicken Kebabs

Kcal	Fat	Saturates	Carbs	Sugars	Protein	Fibre	Salt
267	4.5g	0.9g	13.2g	12.9g	43.7g	43.7g	2g

Serves: 4   **Prep time:** 70 minutes **Cooking time:** 10 minutes

Ingredients:
- 4 skinless chicken breasts (approx.160g each), cut into strips
- 3 tbsps honey
- 3 tbsps soy sauce
- 2 tsps sesame oil
- 1 tsp fresh ginger, finely grated

Instructions:
In a large bowl mix together the honey, soy sauce, sesame oil and fresh ginger.

Add the chicken strips to the marinade and stir until the chicken is evenly coated. Cover the bowl with clingfilm and chill in the fridge for an hour or overnight.

When ready to cook, pre-heat the oven to 190C, 375F, Gas Mark 5. Line a large baking tray with baking parchment or foil.

Thread the chicken strips equally between 12 skewers and lay them on the baking tray. Place in the oven for 25 minutes, turning over after the first 15 minutes.

Fantastic hot or cold served with salad, couscous or rice.

TIP
These can also be cooked on a BBQ.

Fish

Quick Prawn and Courgette Rice

Kcal	Fat	Saturates	Carbs	Sugars	Protein	Fibre	Salt
253	3.3g	1g	33.1g	4.1g	20.6g	0.6g	0.5g

Serves: 2   **Prep time:** 5 minutes   **Cooking time:** 12-15 minutes

Ingredients:
- 1x250g packet of steamed Basmati and Wild rice
- 180g raw peeled king prawns, deveined
- 1 medium courgette, diced
- 1 small red onion, peeled and finely diced
- 1 tsp tomato puree

Instructions:
Heat a frying pan and add a couple of sprays of the rapeseed oil and add the onion. Cook for 1 minute before adding the diced courgetti. Cook for a further 3-4 minutes until the courgette has started to soften.

Add the king prawns and cook for 1-2 minutes until they just start to turn pink, then add 3 tablespoons of water and the tomato puree. Stir to coat all of the ingredients.

Add the rice and cook for a further 3-4 minutes until piping hot and serve straight away.

TIP
If you prefer you can add a few unpeeled prawns to give a more intense flavor.

Cod on a Bed of Smoky Beans

Kcal	Fat	Saturates	Carbs	Sugars	Protein	Fibre	Salt
401	9g	3.1g	27.2g	12g	51.7g	9.6g	1.6g

Serves: 2   **Prep time:** 5 minutes   **Cooking time:** 20 minutes

Ingredients:
- 2x200g skinless cod fillets
- 1 medium red onion, peeled and finely diced
- 1x400g can of chopped tomatoes
- 1x400g can of butter beans, drained
- 50g reduced-fat chorizo
- 1 clove of garlic, peeled and finely diced
- 2 tsp smoked paprika
- A little fresh parsley for garnish
- Black pepper

Instructions:
Preheat the oven to 180C, 350F, Gas Mark 4.

Cook the chorizo in a small pan for 2-3 minutes, then add the onion and garlic and fry gently until soft. Add the tomatoes, paprika, butter beans and season with a little black pepper.

Bring to a simmer and cook for 10-15 mins or until slightly reduced and thickened.

In the mean time place the fish in an ovenproof dish and place in the oven, cook for 15 minutes.

To serve divide the smoky beans between two warm plates and top each with a piece of cod and garnish with the parsley.

Baked Sesame Salmon with Salad

Kcal	Fat	Saturates	Carbs	Sugars	Protein	Fibre	Salt
340	24.3g	4.4g	2.4g	2.4g	28.3g	0.6g	0.3g

Serves: 1   **Prep time:** 5 minutes   **Cooking time:** 14-16 minutes

Ingredients:
- 1x140g fresh salmon fillet
- ½ tsp sesame oil
- ½ tsp sesame seeds
- ½ tsp honey
- Large green salad
- 4 large radishes, sliced
- 1 lime
- Pinch of chilli powder (optional)

Instructions:
Pre-heat the oven to 190C, 375F, gas mark 5.

Place the salmon fillet, skin side down into a shallow oven proof dish.

Brush salmon with the sesame oil, then sprinkle over the sesame seeds, place in the oven and cook for 14-16 minutes.

Arrange the salad and radishes in a pasta bowl, squeeze over the juice of the lime.

Remove the salmon from the oven and cut into chunks, serve hot or cold on the salad. Just before serving sprinkle over a little bit of chilli powder if using.

Simple Fish and Pepper Stew

Kcal	Fat	Saturates	Carbs	Sugars	Protein	Fibre	Salt
257	2.3g	0.4g	20.8g	19.9g	39.1g	6.4g	0.5g

Serves: 2   **Prep time:** 5 minutes   **Cooking time:** 20-25 minutes

Ingredients:
- 2x200g white fish fillets
- 1 medium onion, peeled and finely diced
- 1x400g can of chopped tomatoes
- 1 small red pepper, deseeded and sliced
- 1 small orange pepper, deseeded and sliced
- 1 small yellow pepper, deseeded and sliced
- 1 tsp brown sugar
- Juice from 1 lime
- Rapeseed oil spray
- 1 tbsp fresh parsley

Instructions:
Heat a deep non-stick frying pan, and add a couple of sprays of rapeseed oil and gently fry the onions until softened, add the sliced peppers and continue to cook for a further 4-5 minutes.

Add the tomatoes, salt, black pepper, sugar and lemon juice, bring to the boil, then reduce to a simmer.

Place the fish fillets on top of the pepper stew, scatter over the parsley and cover the frying pan with either a piece of foil or a lid, cook for a further 15 minutes until the fish is tender. Serve immediately.

Fish Tacos

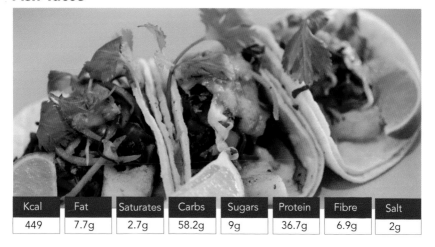

Kcal	Fat	Saturates	Carbs	Sugars	Protein	Fibre	Salt
449	7.7g	2.7g	58.2g	9g	36.7g	6.9g	2g

Serves: 1   **Prep time:** 10 minutes   **Cooking time:** 10 minutes

Ingredients:
- 150g cod fillet
- 3 mini soft tortilla wraps
- 2 limes
- ½ tsp smoked paprika
- ¼ tsp chilli powder
- ¼ tsp garlic powder
- 1 tbsp low fat mayonnaise
- Fresh coriander leaves
- 60g shredded red cabbage
- 1 medium carrot, cut into matchstick size pieces

Instructions:
Remove the skin from the fish and cut into 9 chunks.

Place the garlic powder, chilli powder and smoked paprika into a bowl and mix together.

Pre-heat the oven to 190C, 375F, Gas Mark 5. Line a baking tray with baking parchment.

Place the fish chunks into the spice mix and stir until evenly coated then place the fish onto the baking tray and bake in the oven for 10 minutes or until the fish is opaque.

Mix the mayonnaise with the juice from one of the limes and set aside.

Remove the fish from the oven and place 3 fish chunks in the center of each taco.

Top with shredded cabbage and carrot, drizzle with the lime mayonnaise and top with a few coriander leaves.

Serve straight away with the remaining lime cut into wedges.

Salmon with a Warm Spinach and Chickpea Salad

Kcal	Fat	Saturates	Carbs	Sugars	Protein	Fibre	Salt
504	25.6g	4.2g	24.8g	4.2g	40.6g	6.4g	0.47g

Serves: 1   **Prep time:** 5 minutes   **Cooking time:** 10-15 minutes

Ingredients:
- 1 salmon fillet
- 1x210g can of chickpeas in water, drained
- 2 spring onions, cleaned, trimmed and sliced
- 50g spinach – fresh or frozen
- 5 cherry tomatoes cut in half
- ½ lemon
- Salt and black pepper
- Rapeseed oil spray

Instructions:
Preheat the oven to 200C, 400F or Gas Mark 6

Place the salmon steak on a baking tray and season on both sides with a little salt and black pepper.

Bake in the oven for 10-12 minutes.

In the meantime, heat a small frying pan add a little rapeseed oil spray then add the chopped spring onions and cook for 1-2 minutes.

Add the drained chickpeas to the frying pan along with 1 tbsp of water, season with a little salt and black pepper and cook on a lower heat for a further 3-4 minutes.

Add the spinach and tomato halves to the frying pan, turn up the heat slightly and cook for a further 1-2 minutes until the spinach has wilted.

Remove the salmon from the oven, and gently flake the fish.

Transfer the chickpea and spinach salad to a warmed plate and top with the flaked salmon.

Season with a little more black pepper and squeeze over the juice of half the lemon.

Thai Style Fish Cakes

Kcal	Fat	Saturates	Carbs	Sugars	Protein	Fibre	Salt
267	12g	2.6g	8.2g	3.8g	30.8g	0.7g	1.3g

Serves: 2   **Prep time:** 5 minutes   **Cooking time:** 15 minutes

Ingredients:
- 120g fresh salmon fillet, skin removed
- 150g white fish, skin removed
- 1 red chilli, finely chopped
- 1 egg
- 1 clove of garlic, peeled and finely chopped
- 1 tsp Thai fish sauce
- 1 tsp soy sauce
- 1 stalk of lemon grass, rough outer leaves discarded
- 1 tsp muscovado sugar
- 1 tsp plain flour
- 3 spring onions, finely chopped
- 2 tsps of fresh coriander, finely chopped
- Rapeseed oil spray

Instructions:
Place everything except the spring onions and coriander into a blender. Blend until a rough paste consistency.

Place the paste into a bowl and mix in the spring onions and coriander. Divide the mixture into 6 and make each portion into a small round cake.

Heat a non-stick frying pan and add a little of the rapeseed oil spray, fry in batches of two at a time cooking for 3-4 minutes on each side, ensuring you only turn them once to reduce the risk of them breaking.

Lovely with a large green salad.

King Prawn and Asparagus Linguine

Kcal	Fat	Saturates	Carbs	Sugars	Protein	Fibre	Salt
353	5.3g	0.6g	47g	4.1g	31g	1g	1.3g

Serves: 2   **Prep time:** 10 minutes   **Cooking time:** 20-25 minutes

Ingredients:
- 120g dry linguine pasta
- 1 garlic clove, peeled and finely chopped
- 8 raw, peeled (tails left on and deveined) king prawns
- 8 asparagus spears, woody ends removed and cut in half
- 1 vegetable stock cube
- 6 cherry tomatoes, halved
- Juice and zest of 1 un-waxed lemon
- 1 tsp rapeseed oil
- 1 spring onion, root removed and finely sliced.
- 1 sprig of fresh oregano or a few fresh basil leaves, chopped

Instructions:
Heat a large pan of water and bring to the boil, add the vegetable stock cube and the linguine and cook until the linguine is cooked to your liking.

Heat a frying pan and add the oil, sliced spring onions, asparagus and the garlic, stir and cook for 1-2 minutes.

Add the prawns and cook until pink on both sides and beginning to curl.

Add the cherry tomatoes and cook for a further minute before removing from the heat.

Drain the cooked linguine and place back into the pan. Add the prawn and asparagus mixture with the lemon and herbs to the pasta, stir gently to evenly combine. Serve straight away.

Salmon and Spinach Gnocchi

Kcal	Fat	Saturates	Carbs	Sugars	Protein	Fibre	Salt
625	21g	5.1g	73.4g	1.7g	32.8g	3.8g	1.6g

Serves: 2   **Prep time:** 5 minutes   **Cooking time:** 20 minutes

Ingredients:
- 2 salmon fillets (approx. 120g each), skin removed and cut into chunks
- 2 spring onions, finely sliced
- 1 clove of garlic, peeled and finely diced
- 400g fresh gnocchi
- 2 handfuls of washed spinach leaves
- 1 vegetable stock cube
- Freshly ground black and red peppercorns
- 5g unsalted butter
- A few fresh basil leaves to serve (optional)

Instructions:
Heat a frying pan and add the butter, spring onions and garlic and cook on a low heat to soften.

Add the salmon and increase the heat slightly. Turning the salmon occasionally so not to break up the chunks. After about 3-4 minutes lay add the spinach leaves and black and red pepper and turn down the heat, stirring occasionally.

Bring a large pan of water with the stock cube to the boil.

Add the gnocchi and simmer for 1-2 minutes until the dumplings rise to the surface. Drain and add straight to the salmon and spinach mix.

Gently stir so the gnocchi are covered in the salmon juices.

Serve straight away and sprinkle a few basil leaves over the top.

Easy King Prawn Dhansak Curry

Kcal	Fat	Saturates	Carbs	Sugars	Protein	Fibre	Salt
286	3.5g	0.3g	28g	9g		1.9g	1.9g

Serves: 2   **Prep time:** 5 minutes   **Cooking time:** 25 minutes

Ingredients:
- 1x400g lentil soup
- 300g raw peeled king prawns
- 1 medium white onion, peeled and finely diced
- 1 red chili, finely chopped
- 1 garlic clove, peeled and finely chopped
- 3 tsp's garam masala
- ½ tsp fenugreek (optional)
- 1x200g tin of chopped tomatoes
- A few coriander leaves to serve
- Rapeseed oil spray
- Freshly ground black cracked pepper

Instructions:
Heat a heavy based large saucepan and add a couple of sprays of the rapeseed oil. Add the onion, garlic and chilli cook gently until softened.

Add the garam masala, fenugreek, tomatoes and lentil soup. Stir and reduce to a simmer.

Cook for a further 10 minutes until the sauce has thickened. Now add the raw prawns and stir in and cook for a further 5 minutes until the prawns have turned pink.

Once cooked add the freshly ground black pepper and top with the coriander leaves.

Fantastic served with rice or naan bread and sprinkle a few basil leaves over the top.

Baked Avocado with Smoked Salmon and Eggs

Kcal	Fat	Saturates	Carbs	Sugars	Protein	Fibre	Salt
277	23.5g	5.3g	1.6g	0.5g	14.8g	0.1g	1g

Serves: 2   **Prep time:** 5 minutes   **Cooking time:** 15 minutes

Ingredients:
- 1 medium ripe avocado
- 2 small hens eggs
- 50g sliced smoked salmon
- Freshly ground black pepper
- 1tsp tomato puree
- Pinch of chilli flakes
- A few fresh parsley leaves (optional)

Instructions:
Preheat the oven to 200C, Gas Mark 6, 400F.

Cut the avocado in half and remove the stone and scoop out a little of the flesh to make the hole very slightly deeper, if the stone is small.

Place the avocado halves on a non-stick baking tray.

Divide the smoked salmon into two and line the avocado hole, pushing down slightly.

Crack one egg into each hole.

Bake for 15 minutes or until yolk reaches desired consistency.

Sprinkle over freshly ground black pepper and serve.

Tuna Rice Salad

Kcal	Fat	Saturates	Carbs	Sugars	Protein	Fibre	Salt
376	9.9g	1.6g	45.5g	8.1g	26.8g	4.1g	1g

Serves: 1   **Prep time:** 5 minutes   **Cooking time:** 15-20 minutes

Ingredients:
- 40g basmati rice (dry weight)
- 80g of tinned tuna in brine, drained
- 1 tbsp frozen or tinned sweetcorn
- ½ a red onion, peeled and sliced or 2 spring onions sliced
- 6 cherry or small tomatoes halved
- 4 olives – sliced (optional)
- Juice of one lemon
- ½ tsp dried mixed herbs
- ½ tsp olive oil
- Fresh parsley - optional

Instructions:
Bring a pan of water to the boil and add the rice and sweetcorn, cook for 15 or until your liking. Drain and rinse under cold water to completely cool the rice and sweetcorn.

Add the lemon juice, herbs and olive oil to a small bowl and mix to make a dressing.

Place the rice in a bowl, gently flake in the tuna and add the remaining ingredients.

Pour over the lemon and herb dressing. Gently toss to combine.

Serve straight away with the parsley if using or keep in the fridge for 24 hours.

Baked Salmon with Fennel and Lemon

Kcal	Fat	Saturates	Carbs	Sugars	Protein	Fibre	Salt
323	21.3g	3.9g	2.9g	2.8g	29.9g	0.4g	0.19g

Serves: 2   **Prep time:** 5 minutes   **Cooking time:** 20 minutes

Ingredients:
- 2x140g salmon fillets
- 1 fennel bulb, sliced
- 1 lemon, sliced
- Freshly ground black pepper

Instructions:
Preheat the oven to 200C, 400F, Gas Mark 6.

Place a large piece of baking parchment on a baking tray.

Lay the slices of fennel in the middle of the baking parchment.

Place the salmon fillets on top of the fennel slices (skin side down) , season with some black pepper.

Divide the lemon slices over the top of the salmon fillets.

Take another piece of baking parchment and lay over the top. Roll up the edges to make a sealed bag.

Place in the oven and cook for 20 minutes.

Remove from the oven and leave to rest for 2-3 minutes. Carefully open the parchment bag.

Serve hot or cold.

Pan Fried Mackerel with a Potato and Beetroot Salad

Kcal	Fat	Saturates	Carbs	Sugars	Protein	Fibre	Salt
385	18.4g	3.4g	30.6g	9.6g	21.8g	2.7g	0.4g

Serves: 1   **Prep time:** 5 minutes   **Cooking time:** 20 minutes

Ingredients:
• 1 fresh mackerel fillet, cut in half lengthways and the bones removed
• 1 spring onion, cleaned, root removed and sliced
• 150g pre-cooked baby new potatoes cut in half
• 70g cooked beetroot, cut into wedges
• 1 tbsp reduced-fat mayonnaise
• Juice and zest of a lemon

Instructions:
In a small bowl place the mayonnaise add the zest and juice of the lemon. Gently stir until combined. Add the cold potatoes, spring onion and beetroot wedges to the bowl, and gently stir until evenly coated in the dressing. Then set aside.

Heat a small frying pan. Season the mackerel with the black pepper. When the pan is hot place the mackerel fillets skin side down into the frying pan and cook for 1-2 minutes. Turn the fish over and cook on the other side for a further minute, then remove from the heat.

To serve, place the salad on a plate and then top with the cooked mackerel.

Serve straight away.

Quick Fish Curry

Kcal	Fat	Saturates	Carbs	Sugars	Protein	Fibre	Salt
194	3.4g	0.6g	14.1g	8.9g	29.7g	1.7g	0.70g

Serves: 2   **Prep time:** 5 minutes   **Cooking time:** 15-20 minutes

Ingredients:
- 300g white fish, skin removed and cut into large chunks
- 220ml coconut milk
- 1 medium white onion, peeled and finely chopped
- 1 tbsp garam masala
- 1 tsp turmeric
- ½ tsp fennel seeds
- 1 tsp ground cumin
- 1cm piece of fresh root ginger, peeled and grated
- 1 clove of garlic, peeled and finely chopped
- 1 tbsp fresh coriander, chopped
- ½ green chili deseeded and finely diced

Instructions:
Heat a large non-stick frying pan to a medium heat. Add the onion and garlic and cook gently until softened.

Add the garam masala, turmeric, fennel seeds, ginger and ground cumin. Cook for a further couple of minutes.

Add the coconut milk and reduce the heat to a simmer for 3-4 minutes.

Add the fish and cook for a further 5-10 minutes until tender, stirring occasionally.

Just before serving stir in the coriander and serve with the fresh green chilli sprinkled over the top. Great served with rice or a naan bread.

Veggie

Cheese Quesadillas

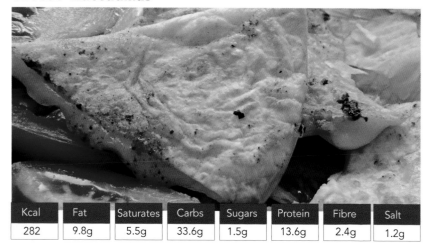

Kcal	Fat	Saturates	Carbs	Sugars	Protein	Fibre	Salt
282	9.8g	5.5g	33.6g	1.5g	13.6g	2.4g	1.2g

Serves: 1   **Prep time:** 2 minutes   **Cooking time:** 8 minutes

Ingredients:
- 2 plain mini tortilla wraps
- 30g reduced-fat cheddar cheese

Instructions:
Preheat a small frying pan. Place one tortilla wrap in the pan and top with the grated cheese and a little black pepper, then top with the remaining wrap.

Cook for 3-4 minutes on one side then carefully turn over the Quesadilla and cook on the other side for 2-3 minutes or until the cheese is melted and the wraps have taken on a golden colour.

Remove from the frying pan, place on a chopping board and cut into 4.

Serve straight away - be careful as the inside will be hot.

TIP
Use plant-based cheese to make it vegan friendly.

Easy Stuffed Mexican Egg Peppers

Kcal	Fat	Saturates	Carbs	Sugars	Protein	Fibre	Salt
310	8.3g	2.3g	39.3g	12.1g	16g	10.4g	3.2g

Serves: 4   **Prep time:** 10 minutes   **Cooking time:** 35 minutes

Ingredients:
- 4 red peppers
- 1x395g can taco mixed beans in spicy sauce
- 4 medium eggs
- 1x250g packet Mexican style microwaveable rice
- 3 tbsps water

Instructions:
Preheat the oven to 200C, 400F, Gas Mark 6

Carefully cut the tops off each pepper. Gently remove the seeds and discard them.

In a clean bowl add the rice and gently fluff up with a fork. Add the taco mixed beans and the water and mix until evenly combined.

Divide the mixture between the four peppers.

Place the peppers into a shallow oven proof dish that will allow them to stay upright when cooking.

Using a teaspoon make a small well in the middle of the rice mixture in each pepper. Carefully crack an egg and gently slide it into the well taking care not to break the yolk. Repeat with the remaining eggs and peppers.

Place the tops of the peppers back on the filled pepper bases and cook in the oven for 25-35 minutes until cooked through. Serve straight away.

TIP
Perfect as a lunch with a green salad or with sausages for a main meal.

Three Bean Enchiladas

Kcal	Fat	Saturates	Carbs	Sugars	Protein	Fibre	Salt
496	13g	5g	73.1g	14g	23.7g	6.6g	1.7g

Serves: 4   **Prep time:** 10 minutes   **Cooking time:** 30 minutes

Ingredients:
- 4 soft tortilla wraps
- 4 tbsp Sarah's BBQ Sauce (see page **158**)
- 1x350g Jar of Cirio Passata Rustica (or use ordinary tomato passata)
- 1 green chilli, deseeded and finely diced
- 6 spring onions, roots removed and finely sliced
- 2 cloves of garlic, peeled and finely diced
- 1 large carrot, peeled and grated
- 1x210g can of chickpeas in water, drained
- 1x210g can of kidney beans in water, drained
- 1x400g can of borlotti beans in water, drained
- 1x200g can of sweetcorn in water, drained
- Salt and pepper to season
- ½ tsp paprika
- 80g grated reduced fat cheddar style cheese
- 1 tsp rapeseed oil

Instructions:
Preheat the oven to 190C, 375F, Gas Mark 5.

Heat a frying pan and add the oil, spring onions (keep ½ tbsp back for decoration) garlic, grated carrot, paprika and chilli. Cook for 2-3 minutes until the carrot has started to soften.

Add the chickpeas, borlotti, sweetcorn and kidney beans to the frying pan and stir, cook for a further 1-2 minutes and then add the passata and stir to combine the ingredients. Cook on a medium heat for a further 5 minutes until the sauce has thickened. Season with the salt and pepper and remove from the heat.

Take a quarter of the bean mixture and place it in the center of a tortilla and gently roll up, place in an oven proof dish and repeat with the remaining mixture and tortilla wraps.

Gently cover the top of the enchiladas with the BBQ sauce and top with the grated cheese. Put in the oven and bake for 15 minutes or until the cheese is bubbling.

Remove from the oven and sprinkle with the remaining spring onion slices. Serve straight away.

Cheesy Vegetable Pasta

Kcal	Fat	Saturates	Carbs	Sugars	Protein	Fibre	Salt
345	9.1g	4.5g	46.1g	5g	18.8g	5.9g	1.5g

Serves: 1   **Prep time:** 5 minutes   **Cooking time:** 20 minutes

Ingredients:
- 50g pasta shapes, dry weight
- 140g frozen mixed vegetables
- 1 vegetable stock cube
- 30g reduced-fat cheddar cheese, finely grated
- Black pepper

Instructions:
Three quarters fill a medium sized saucepan with water. Add the stock cube and bring to the boil.

Add the pasta shapes and cook for 15 minutes.

Add the frozen vegetables and bring back to the boil and cook for a further 3-4 minutes.

Drain the pasta and vegetables and return to the saucepan. Add the grated cheese and stir gently to combine. The heat from the saucepan and the pasta and vegetables will naturally melt the cheese.

Season with a little black pepper and serve straight away.

Tomato and Basil Gnocchi

Kcal	Fat	Saturates	Carbs	Sugars	Protein	Fibre	Salt
310	8.3g	2.3g	39.3g	12.1g	16g	10.4g	3.2g

Serves: 2   **Prep time:** 5 minutes   **Cooking time:** 15 minutes

Ingredients:
- 1x350g jar of Cirio Passata Rustica (ordinary passata can be used)
- 5 spring onions, finely sliced
- 1 clove of garlic, peeled and finely diced
- 400g fresh gnocchi
- 1 small handful of basil leaves, finely chopped
- 1 vegetable stock cube
- Freshly ground black pepper
- Rapeseed oil spray
- A few fresh basil leaves to serve
- A little fresh vegetarian style Parmesan to serve (optional)

Instructions:
Heat a frying pan and add a couple of sprays of the oil, spring onions and garlic and cook on a low heat to soften.

Add the tomato passata and increase the heat slightly. After a about 3-4 minutes add the chopped basil leaves and black pepper and turn down the heat, stirring occasionally.

Bring a large pan of water with the stock cube to the boil.

Add the gnocchi and simmer for 1-2 minutes until the dumplings rise to the surface. Drain and add straight to the tomato sauce and stir gently.

Serve straight away and sprinkle a few basil leaves and cheese over the top if required.

TIP
To spice it up add ½ a chopped red chilli when you cook the onions and garlic.

Quick and Simple Pea Soup

Kcal	Fat	Saturates	Carbs	Sugars	Protein	Fibre	Salt
158	2.2g	0.3g	24.2g	13.8g	11.3g	11.7g	0.67g

Serves: 2   **Prep time:** 5 minutes   **Cooking time:** 10 minutes

Ingredients:
- 400g frozen peas
- 1 medium onion, peeled and finely chopped
- 500ml vegetable stock
- Rapeseed oil spray
- Salt and freshly ground black pepper
- Few sprigs of fresh mint (optional)
- 2 tsps of Greek yoghurt (optional)

Instructions:
Heat a couple of sprays of the oil in a large saucepan on low or medium heat, then add the onion and cook for 1-2 minutes until softened.

Add the peas and stock to the pan, then bring to the boil.

Cook for 5-8 minutes until all of the peas have floated to the top of the stock and are tender and the fresh mint (keep a couple of leaves for serving) and cook for a further 2 minutes.

Remove the pan from the heat. Using a stick blender, process the peas mixture until very smooth. If using a jug blender allow to cool for a few minutes before transferring, be careful of the steam as you pour.

Blitz until smooth and serve straight away. Decorate with a little yoghurt if using and a couple of mint leaves.

To make this dairy free and vegan omit the yoghurt.

Quorn Marsala with Pasta

Kcal	Fat	Saturates	Carbs	Sugars	Protein	Fibre	Salt
374	5g	1.9g	45g	8.6g	31.6g	11.3g	1.7g

Serves: 2   **Prep time:** 5 minutes **Cooking time:** 25 minutes

Ingredients:
- 240g Quorn fillets, sliced
- 1 small white onion, peeled and finely diced
- 100g chestnut mushrooms, cleaned and sliced
- 100g dry spaghetti or linguine pasta
- 150g low-fat cream cheese
- 50ml Marsala wine, sherry or port
- 1 clove of garlic, peeled and finely diced
- Salt and black pepper for seasoning
- Rapeseed oil spray

Instructions:
Bring a large pan of water to the boil and add the pasta.

Preheat a frying pan and add a couple of sprays of rapeseed oil. Add the diced onion and cook for 2-3 minutes until starting to soften.

Add the Quorn slices and the mushrooms to the onions and cook for a further 3-4 minutes, then add the Marsala wine, sherry or port to the pan and stir gently.

Add the cream cheese to the Quorn and mushroom mixture, reduce the heat and stir gently until the cream cheese melts down into a sauce, about 2-3 minutes - (if it's a little thick add a little milk). Season with the black pepper and salt.

Remove the pasta from the heat and drain. Divide the pasta between two warmed pasta bowls. Top with the Quorn mixture, garnish with the parsley and serve straight away.

Vegan Cheesy Cottage Pie

Kcal	Fat	Saturates	Carbs	Sugars	Protein	Fibre	Salt
548	7.7g	3.2g	92.7g	23.1g	28.8g	10.3g	1g

Serves: 1   **Prep time:** 5 minutes   **Cooking time:** 50-55 minutes

Ingredients:
- 50g puy/green lentils
- 20g red split lentils
- 1 small red onion, peeled and finely diced
- 1 medium carrot, peeled and grated
- 1 tbsp frozen peas
- 100g sweet potato, peeled and cut into small chunks
- 100g white potato, peeled and cut into small chunks
- 200ml vegetable stock
- 1 tsp tomato puree
- ½ tsp soy sauce
- Rapeseed oil spray
- Salt and black pepper
- 20g reduced-fat vegan style cheddar cheese

Instructions:
Preheat the oven to 200C, 400F, Gas Mark 6.

Boil the potatoes together in a saucepan of water until soft.

Heat a frying pan and add a couple of sprays of rapeseed oil and add the onions and fry until they start to go brown. Add the puy, red lentils and grated carrot and continue to cook for a further 2-3 minutes.

Add the stock, tomato puree and soy sauce to the lentil mixture, stir and reduce the heat slightly and add the frozen peas and cook for 15-20 minutes until the lentils have cooked.

Drain the potatoes and mash well, seasoning with salt and black pepper. Stir in the grated cheese.

Transfer the lentil mixture to a small ovenproof dish and spread the mashed cheesy potato over the top.

Bake in the oven for 20 minutes, or until the top has started to go brown.

Tomato and Olive Pasta

Kcal	Fat	Saturates	Carbs	Sugars	Protein	Fibre	Salt
265	7g	1g	41.2g	5.8g	8.8g	2.3g	1.7g

Serves: 1   **Prep time:** 5 minutes   **Cooking time:** 20 minutes

Ingredients:
- 45g pasta spirals (dry weight)
- 100g tomato passata
- 2 spring onions, cleaned, root removed and thinly sliced
- 8 black olives, each sliced into 3 pieces
- Large handful green salad leaves such as rocket
- 1 vegetable stock cube
- Freshly ground black pepper to season

Instructions:
Heat a large pan of water with the stock cube dissolved in it. Bring to the boil then add the pasta shapes and reduce the heat slightly.

In the meantime heat a small frying pan and add a couple of sprays of rapeseed oil and gently cook the spring onions for 2-3 minutes. Add the tomato passata and black pepper to taste and cook for 3-4 minutes until the sauce has reduced slightly.

Drain the pasta shapes and return to the pan, add tomato sauce and stir to combine.

Serve in a warmed pasta bowl, topped with the green salad leaves and sprinkle over the sliced black olives.

Sweet Potato with Spicy Salsa, Chickpeas and Avocado

Kcal	Fat	Saturates	Carbs	Sugars	Protein	Fibre	Salt
405	22.8g	4.7g	44.7g	14.1g	8g	5.1g	0.75g

Serves: 1   **Prep time:** 10 minutes   **Cooking time:** 50 minutes

Ingredients:
- 1x150g sweet potato
- 1 medium avocado
- 40g canned chickpeas (drained weight)
- ½ small red chilli, deseeded and finely diced
- 2 medium ripe tomatoes
- 2 tsps tomato puree
- Freshly ground black pepper
- Few coriander leaves (optional)

Instructions:
Preheat the oven to 180C, 350F, Gas Mark 4.

Wipe the potato with a damp cloth and then prick all over and bake in the oven for 40-50 minutes.

Place the chopped tomatoes, tomato puree, chopped chilli (reserve a little for garnish), chickpeas and freshly ground black pepper in a bowl and gently mix until combined. Cover with clingfilm and place in the fridge until required.

Remove the jacket potato from the oven and place on a serving plate and cut down the centre lengthways, place the salsa bean filling on top.

Cut the avocado in half and remove the stone. Peel away the skin and discard. Roughly chop the flesh and place on top of the salsa. Add a few chopped fresh coriander leaves and serve straight away.

Roasted Ratatouille

Kcal	Fat	Saturates	Carbs	Sugars	Protein	Fibre	Salt
137	2.3g	0.3g	23.2g	21g	6.7g	6.2g	0.3g

Serves: 2   **Prep time:** 5 minutes **Cooking time:** 30 minutes

Ingredients:
- 1 large aubergine, stalk removed and cut into 2cm chunks
- 2 medium courgettes, tops removed and cut into 1cm chunks
- 1 large red onion, peeled and cut into chunks
- 1 red pepper, deseeded and cut into 1cm chunks
- 2 cloves of garlic, peeled and cut into slices
- 2 large ripe tomatoes, cut into quarters
- 1x400g can chopped tomatoes
- 1 ½ tsps mixed dried Italian style herbs
- 1 tsp tomato puree
- Rapeseed oil spray
- Salt and black pepper

Instructions:
Pre-heat the oven to 190C, 375F, Gas Mark 5.

Scatter the chopped vegetables and garlic onto a non-stick baking tray. Spray lightly with the rapeseed oil spray and season with a little salt and black pepper. Place in the oven and roast for 15-20 minutes.

Remove the vegetables from the oven and carefully transfer to a large saucepan. Add canned chopped tomatoes, tomato puree and dried herbs. Gently bring to the boil, then reduce to a simmer and cook for 5-10 until the liquid has thickened.

Serve hot or cold.

TIP
Put any leftover ratatouille into a blender and blitz to make a quick pasta sauce!

Bow Pasta with Quorn

Kcal	Fat	Saturates	Carbs	Sugars	Protein	Fibre	Salt
405	5g	0.9g	63.6g	5.7g	28g	11.3g	2.3g

Serves: 1   **Prep time:** 5 minutes **Cooking time:** 15-20 minutes

Ingredients:
- 80g Farfalle (bow) pasta
- 120g Quorn pieces
- 120g tomato passata
- 1tsp mixed dried herbs
- 1 vegetable stock cube
- Rapeseed oil spray
- Black pepper to season
- A few basil leaves to garnish - optional

Instructions:
Three quarters fill a medium sized saucepan with water and add the stock cube, place on the heat and bring to the boil. Add the pasta bows, and reduce the heat slightly.

While the pasta is cooking, heat a small frying pan and add a couple of sprays of rapeseed oil. Add the Quorn and cook for 3-5 minutes until starting to brown.

Add the dried herbs and tomato passata, stir to combine and reduce the heat to a simmer and cook for 10 minutes.

Once the pasta is cooked, drain and return to the pan. Remove the Quorn and tomato mixture from the heat and add to the pasta. Stir gently and season with the black pepper.

Serve in a warmed pasta bowl, topped with a little fresh basil (optional).

Falafel Burgers

Kcal	Fat	Saturates	Carbs	Sugars	Protein	Fibre	Salt
386	6.8g	1.5g	62.2g	4.8g	16.5g	6.8g	0.83g

Serves: 2   **Prep time:** 25 minutes **Cooking time:** 10 minutes

Ingredients:
- 2 burger baps
- 1x200g tin of chickpeas in water, drained
- 1 spring onion, cleaned, root removed and cut in half
- ½ tsp Harrisa Spice Mix
- 1 ½ tsp plain flour
- 1 garlic clove peeled
- 1 small handful fresh parsley
- 1 large handful coriander
- Rapeseed oil spray
- Mixed salad leaves to garnish (optional)

Instructions:
Place the chickpeas, parsley, coriander, garlic, flour, harissa spice mix and spring onion into a small blender or food processor and blend until smooth.

Divide the burger mixture in half and shape each portion into a burger. Gently wrap in clingfilm and chill for 20 minutes.

When you are ready to cook the burgers, preheat a frying pan, add a couple of sprays of the rapeseed oil and add the burgers. Cook on each side for 4-5 minutes until piping hot and slightly golden on the outside.

To serve, place each burger in the roll and top each burger with the salad if using - serve straight away.

Wild Mushroom Risotto

Kcal	Fat	Saturates	Carbs	Sugars	Protein	Fibre	Salt
428	2.5g	0.3g	83.3g	2.9g	10g	2.2g	0.46g

Serves: 2   **Prep time:** 5 minutes   **Cooking time:** 20 minutes

Ingredients:
- 100g wild mixed mushrooms
- 50g chestnut mushrooms, sliced
- 120g Arborio Risotto rice
- 100ml dry white wine
- 1 small onion, peeled and finely diced
- 500ml vegetable stock
- 1 clove of garlic, peeled and finely diced
- ½ tsp dried tarragon
- Rapeseed oil spray
- Black pepper

Instructions:
Heat a heavy based medium saucepan. Add a couple of sprays of the rapeseed oil and add the diced onion and garlic and cook for 2-3 minutes over a medium heat until the onions and garlic have started to soften.

Add the mushrooms and cook for a further 2-3 minutes. Now add the rice and cook for a further 2-3 minutes.

Pour in the wine and simmer, stirring, until the liquid has been absorbed. Add the dried tarragon and a quarter of the stock and simmer, stirring again, until the liquid has been absorbed. Continue adding the stock in this way, until all the liquid has been absorbed and the rice has swelled and is tender.

Season with the black pepper and serve straight away.

Simple Quorn Korma

Kcal	Fat	Saturates	Carbs	Sugars	Protein	Fibre	Salt
342	8.4g	1.3g	40.2g	16.9g	30.5g	17.6g	2.1g

Serves: 1   **Prep time:** 5 minutes **Cooking time:** 20 minutes

Ingredients:
- 150g Quorn Vegan Pieces
- 200ml of coconut milk
- 1 small onion, peeled and finely diced onion
- 1.5 tsp plain flour (00 grade is best)
- 2 tsp Garam Masala or curry powder
- ½ tsp turmeric
- ½ tsp ground cumin
- ¼ tsp chilli powder
- 1 cm cube of fresh ginger peeled and finely chopped or grated
- 1 small clove of garlic peeled and finely chopped
- 1 tbsp fresh coriander roughly chopped
- 50ml milk
- Rapeseed oil spray

Instructions:
Add the flour and the Quorn pieces to a medium sized bowl and stir until the Quorn is evenly coated in the flour.

Heat a non-stick saucepan and add a couple of sprays of rapeseed oil, onion and garlic and cook until soft.

Add the garam masala, ginger and turmeric to the onion/garlic mixture, stir and cook for 1 minute.

Add the Quorn pieces and excess flour to the saucepan and stir to evenly coat with the spice mixture. Continue cooking until the Quorn has been sealed and is starting to take on the colour of the spices.

Gently add the coconut milk and the milk. Slowly bring to the boil, stirring all the time to ensure the sauce does not split, reduce to a simmer and cook for a further 10–15 minutes until the sauce has thickened. Just before serving stir in the fresh coriander and serve.

Sweet Potato and Okra Stew

Kcal	Fat	Saturates	Carbs	Sugars	Protein	Fibre	Salt
243	4.2g	0.7g	47.4g	18.4g	7.5g	2.6g	0.66g

Serves: 2   **Prep time:** 10 minutes   **Cooking time:** 25 minutes

Ingredients:
- 350g sweet potatoes peeled and cut into 1cm cubes
- 200g okra, top and tailed and cut into 1cm chunks
- 8 cherry tomatoes, cut in half
- 1 large white onion, peeled, cut in half and sliced
- 500ml hot vegetable stock
- ½ tsp garam masala
- ½ tsp fennel seeds
- ½ tsp cumin seeds
- ¼ tsp turmeric
- Freshly ground back pepper
- Rapeseed oil spray

Instructions:
Heat a large frying pan and add a couple of sprays of rapeseed oil. Add the onions, sweet potato, fennel seeds, garam masala, turmeric and cumin seeds and cook for 3-4 minutes stirring occasionally.

Add the okra, and gently pour in the hot vegetable stock, reduce the heat to a simmer and cook for 10-15 minutes.

Add the tomatoes and cook for a further 3-4 minutes, if there is still a lot of liquid, just bring to the boil for a couple of minutes until reduced.

Season with the salt and black pepper and serve straight away.

Indian Style Roasted Cauliflower Steak

Kcal	Fat	Saturates	Carbs	Sugars	Protein	Fibre	Salt
154	8.1g	0.8g	17g	12.1g	9.6g	5.4g	0.11g

Serves: 1　　**Prep time:** 5 minutes　**Cooking time:** 20 minutes

Ingredients:
- 2 large slices of cauliflower, cut approx. 1.5 cm thick
- 1 clove of garlic peeled, and slightly crushed
- 1tsp rapeseed oil
- 1 tsp golden syrup
- ½ tsp turmeric
- ¼ tsp fennel seeds
- ¼ tsp mustard seeds
- ¼ tsp ground cumin

Instructions:
Preheat the oven to 200C, Gas Mark 6, 400F
In a small bowl mix together the turmeric, rapeseed oil, golden syrup, mustard seeds, fennel seeds and ground cumin to form a paste.

Brush both sides of the cauliflower slices with the spicy paste mix and lay on a non-stick baking tray. Lay the crushed garlic in between the cauliflower slices.

Bake in the oven for 15-20 minutes until golden.

When cooked discard the garlic and serve immediately – sprinkle over some fresh herbs (optional).

Potato, Mushroom and Pea Bake

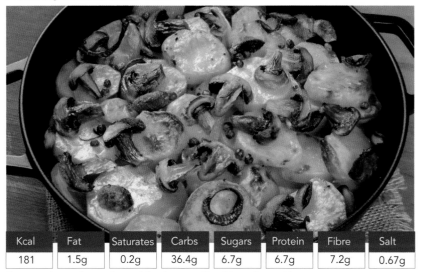

Kcal	Fat	Saturates	Carbs	Sugars	Protein	Fibre	Salt
181	1.5g	0.2g	36.4g	6.7g	6.7g	7.2g	0.67g

Serves: 2 **Prep time:** 10 minutes **Cooking time:** 60 minutes

Ingredients:
- 300g Maris Piper potatoes (or similar), peeled and cut into 0.5cm thick slices
- 200g chestnut mushrooms, cleaned and sliced
- 1 red onion, peeled, cut in half and sliced
- 500ml hot vegetable stock
- 80g frozen peas
- 1tsp fresh rosemary
- Freshly ground back pepper
- Rapeseed oil spray

Instructions:
Preheat the oven to 190C, Gas Mark 5, 375F

Take a oven proof dish, place half of the sliced potatoes on the bottom of the dish, sprinkle over half of the frozen peas, sliced mushrooms and onions and a little freshly ground black pepper and the Rosemary. Repeat the process with the remaining vegetables.

Gently pour over the hot vegetable stock.

Spray the top with a little of the rapeseed oil spray and loosely cover in foil (shiny side down) and place in the oven for 50 minutes.

After cooking for 50 minutes, remove the foil and cook for a further 10 minutes until the top starts to brown slightly.

Remove from the oven and allow to stand for 3-5 minutes before serving.

Quick Mexican Rice and Quinoa Salad

Kcal	Fat	Saturates	Carbs	Sugars	Protein	Fibre	Salt
387	19.9g	4g	41.4g	6.6g	10.1g	5.2g	0.6g

Serves: 2   **Prep time:** 5 minutes   **Cooking time:** 8-10 minutes

Ingredients:
- 1x250g packet of ready cooked Vegetable & Quinoa steamed basmati rice
- 2 spring onions, cleaned, root removed and sliced
- 50g frozen or tinned sweetcorn
- 1x200g can of kidney beans, drained
- 1 medium avocado, peeled, stone removed and diced
- 4 small tomatoes, quartered
- 1 tsp chilli powder
- 1 clove of garlic, peeled and diced
- Rapeseed oil spray
- Fresh parlsey to garnish - optional

Instructions:
Heat a frying pan and add a couple of sprays of rapeseed oil. Add the spring onions, garlic, tomatoes, sweetcorn and kidney beans and cook for 2-3 minutes.

Add the rice mix and the chilli powder to the frying pan with 3 tablespoons of water and cook for a further 3-4 minutes, stirring occasionally.

Remove from the heat and gently stir in the chopped avocado and serve straight away with a little fresh parsley.

TIP
Allow to rice mix to cool completely and then add the avocado, if you prefer the salad cold.

Feta Style Bean Wraps

Kcal	Fat	Saturates	Carbs	Sugars	Protein	Fibre	Salt
387	13.2g	9.6g	55.5g	4.9g	12.8g	3.6g	1.6g

Serves: 1   **Prep time:** 5 minutes **Cooking time:** 10 minutes

Ingredients:
- 2 mini soft tortilla wraps
- 1 tomato, cut into 8 wedges
- 100g canned kidney beans, drained and rinsed
- 30g plant based feta style cheese, crumbled
- 1tsp tomato puree
- Pinch of chilli flakes
- A few fresh parsley leaves (optional)

Instructions:
Pre-heat the oven to 200C, Gas Mark 6, 400F.

In a small bowl add the kidney beans, chilli flakes, crumbled feta style cheese, tomato wedges and tomato puree. Gently stir to combine. If using add the parsley leaves.

Divide the mixture in half and place down the center of each wrap. Roll into a tube and place on a non-stick baking tray.

Bake in the oven for 10 minutes, or until the wrap is just starting to brown.

Serve straight away.

Mushroom and Cauliflower Pasta

Kcal	Fat	Saturates	Carbs	Sugars	Protein	Fibre	Salt
368	8g	3.7g	63.1g	6g	13.5g	3.5g	2g

Serves: 1   **Prep time:** 5 minutes   **Cooking time:** 20 minutes

Ingredients:
- 70g pasta bows (dry weight)
- 150g cauliflower, broken into small florets
- 100g chestnut mushrooms, cleaned and sliced
- 1 vegetable stock cube
- 20g finely grated plant-based Parmesan style cheese
- 1 tbs chopped parsley leaves
- Rapeseed oil spray
- Freshly ground black pepper to season

Instructions:
Heat a large pan of water with the stock cube dissolved in it. Bring to the boil then add the pasta shapes and reduce the heat slightly.

In the meantime heat a frying pan, add a couple of sprays of the rapeseed oil and then add the mushrooms and cauliflower florets, cook until the cauliflower is still crunchy but has taken on some colour.

Drain the pasta shapes and return to the pan, add the cooked mushrooms and cauliflower, season with the black pepper and add the parsley, and stir gently then serve in a warmed pasta bowl and sprinkle over the grated cheese.

			...rbs	Sugars	Protein	Fibre	Salt
	3.7g	0.4g	23.2g	19.7g	6.4g	11g	0.94g

Serves: 1   **Prep time:** 5 minutes **Cooking time:** 8-12 minutes

Ingredients:
- 1 small red pepper, deseeded and diced
- 1 small yellow pepper, deseeded and diced
- 1 clove of garlic, peeled and finely chopped
- 50g french green beans, top and tailed
- 1 small red onion, peeled, cut in half and sliced
- 3 tomatoes, roughly chopped
- 150g chestnut mushrooms
- 3tsp Piri Piri sauce
- 1tsp soy sauce
- Rapeseed oil spray

Instructions:
Preheat a non-stick wok or large frying pan, add a couple of sprays of the rapeseed oil then add the onion, mushrooms and garlic and dry-fry until soft. Add the green beans, red and yellow pepper, and cook for a further 4-5 minutes.

Add the chopped tomatoes, soy sauce and lime juice, then stir in the piri piri sauce, and cook for 3-4 minutes, tossing well, until the vegetables are just tender.

Serve straight away.

Sweet Potato Soup

Kcal	Fat	Saturates	Carbs	Sugars	Protein	Fibre	Salt
273	3.6g	0.4g	59.1g	17.3g	4.5g	0.9g	1.4g

Serves: 2 **Prep time:** 5 minutes **Cooking time:** 10 minutes

Ingredients:
- 2 medium sweet potatoes (approx. 550g) – oven baked in their skins and cooled
- 400ml of vegetable stock
- 1 medium onion, peeled and sliced
- Pinch of sea salt
- 1 large clove of garlic, peeled and chopped
- 1 tsp ground cumin
- ½ tsp rapeseed oil
- Freshly ground black pepper to taste
- 1tsp fresh parsley or coriander (optional)

Instructions:
Cut the cooled cooked baked sweet potatoes in half and scoop out the soft flesh into a saucepan.

Heat a frying pan, add the oil and then add the shallots and garlic and cook on a medium heat for 2-3 minutes. Add the salt and cumin and cook for a further minute.

Pour 300ml of the stock into the saucepan with the sweet potatoes and slowly bring to the boil.

Whilst this is happening take the frying pan of the heat and gently add the remaining stock. Stir to release everything from the bottom of the pan. Gently pour the ingredients into the saucepan with the sweet potatoes and stock.

Reduce the heat to a simmer and cook for a further 5 minutes.

Once cooked, allow to cool slightly before blending the soup until smooth. Season to taste with the black pepper.

Vegetarian Cheesy Cottage Pie

Kcal	Fat	Saturates	Carbs	Sugars	Protein	Fibre	Salt
424	8.2g	3.5g	60g	22.5g	28.7g	20.3g	1.9g

Serves: 1   **Prep time:** 5 minutes   **Cooking time:** 45-50 minutes

Ingredients:
- 130g Quorn mince
- 1 small red onion, peeled and finely diced
- 1 medium carrot, peeled and grated
- 1 tbsp frozen peas
- 100g sweet potato, peeled and cut into small chunks
- 100g white potato, peeled and cut into small chunks
- 150ml vegetable stock
- 1 tsp tomato puree
- ½ tsp soy sauce
- Rapeseed oil spray
- Salt and black pepper
- 20g reduced-fat cheddar cheese

Instructions:
Preheat the oven to 200C, 400F, Gas Mark 6.

Boil the potatoes together in a saucepan of water until soft.

Heat a frying pan and add a couple of sprays of rapeseed oil and add the onions and fry until they start to go brown. Add the Quorn Mince and grated carrot and continue to cook for a further 2-3 minutes.

Add the stock, tomato puree and soy sauce to the mince mixture, stir and reduce the heat slightly and add the frozen peas.

Drain the potatoes and mash well, seasoning with salt and black pepper. Stir in the grated cheese.

Transfer the mince mixture to a small ovenproof dish and spread the mashed cheesy potato over the top.

Bake in the oven for 20 minutes, or until the top has started to go brown.

Mushroom and Banana Blossom Linguine

Kcal	Fat	Saturates	Carbs	Sugars	Protein	Fibre	Salt
374	2.8g	0.4g	63g	3.9g	13.3g	9.4g	0.36g

Serves: 1   **Prep time:** 5 minutes   **Cooking time:** 15 minutes

Ingredients:
- 150g canned banana blossom, drained weight or canned artichoke hearts
- 80g mushrooms, sliced
- 30g fresh spinach, shredded
- 60g linguine pasta (dry weight)
- 80ml dry white wine
- 1 clove of garlic, peeled and finely diced
- 1 vegetable stock cube
- 1 tsp dried mixed herbs
- Rapeseed oil spray
- Vegan style Parmesan cheese for garnish

Instructions:
Bring a saucepan of water to the boil and add the stock cube and linguini pasta, and reduce the heat slightly.

Heat a medium frying pan. Add a couple of sprays of rapeseed oil. Add the garlic and dried herbs and cook for 1 minute.

Add the mushrooms, banana blossom or artichoke hearts, 50ml of water and the white wine.

Cook for 3-4 minutes until the liquid has almost reduced then add the spinach. Stir and remove from the heat.

Drain the pasta, and transfer to a warmed pasta bowl. Pour over the mushrooms, banana blossom and spinach and garnish with a little Vegan style Parmesan cheese.

Aubergine and Lentil Bake

Kcal	Fat	Saturates	Carbs	Sugars	Protein	Fibre	Salt
317	12.7g	7.4g	29g	15g	21.1g	3.8g	0.72g

Serves: 2   **Prep time:** 5 minutes   **Cooking time:** 30 minutes

Ingredients:
- 1 large aubergine
- 1x350g jar Cirio Passata Rustica (or standard passata)
- 50g dry red split lentils
- 100g roughly grated or sliced mozzarella cheese
- 1 yellow pepper, deseeded and cut into 1cm chunks
- 4 spring onions, root removed and finely sliced
- 1 clove of garlic, peeled and finely chopped
- Handful of fresh basil leaves, finely chopped
- Salt and black pepper to season
- Rapeseed oil spray

Instructions:
Pre-heat the oven to 200C

Cut the aubergine in half and carefully scoop out the flesh taking care not to damage the skin. Dice the flesh into large chunks and set aside the skins as they will become the shell for the bake.

Heat a frying pan and add a couple of sprays of the oil. Add the garlic, yellow pepper and spring onions and cook for 1-2 minutes, add the aubergine and cook for a further 2 minutes.

Add the lentils, passata and basil. Stir to combine, bring o the boil and then reduce to a simmer and cook for 15 minutes. Season with the salt and black pepper.

Remove from the heat. Place the aubergine skins onto a non-stick baking tray. Divide the aubergine and lentil mixture between the two aubergine shells. Top with the mozzarella and bake at the top of the oven for 10 minutes or until the cheese is bubbling. Serve straight away.

Roasted Tomato and Pepper Soup

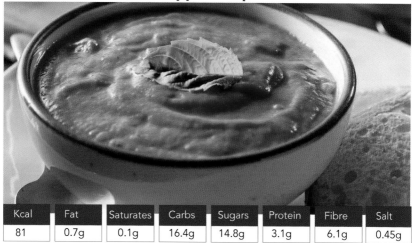

Kcal	Fat	Saturates	Carbs	Sugars	Protein	Fibre	Salt
81	0.7g	0.1g	16.4g	14.8g	3.1g	6.1g	0.45g

Serves: 4 **Prep time:** 10 minutes **Cooking time:** 30 minutes

Ingredients:
- 1kg over-ripe tomatoes, wiped and stalks removed
- 2 red peppers, deseeded and quartered
- 2 large onions, peeled and quartered
- 3 cloves of garlic, peeled
- ½ red chilli, deseeded
- 400ml hot vegetable stock
- Pinch of sea salt
- Black pepper to season

Instructions:
Pre-heat the oven to 190C, 375F, Gas Mark 5.

Place the tomatoes, pepper, garlic, onion and chilli in a shallow baking dish and sprinkle over the salt.

Place in the top of the oven and bake for 30 minutes.

Carefully place the roasted vegetables in a blender or food processor with any juices left over and begin to puree. Slowly add the hot stock until the desired consistency is achieved.

Season with the black pepper.

Warm through in a saucepan if required and serve straight away.

TIPS
- Suitable for freezing.
- This soup makes a great base for a quick pasta sauce!

Quick Seitan Dhansak Curry

Kcal	Fat	Saturates	Carbs	Sugars	Protein	Fibre	Salt
458	5.6g	0.5g	36.5g	6.3g	69.5g	2.5g	1.3g

Serves: 1   **Prep time:** 5 minutes **Cooking time:** 20 minutes

Ingredients:
- 80g seitan – cut in into 8 pieces
- ½ 400g can of lentil soup
- 1 small onion, finely diced
- 1x200g tin of chopped tomatoes
- 1 small clove of garlic, peeled and finely diced
- 1.5 tsp garam masala or curry powder
- ½ tsp turmeric
- ½ tsp cumin seeds
- 1 small red chilli, deseeded and finely diced or 1/3 tsp of dried chilli flakes
- Few fresh coriander leaves to serve
- Rapeseed oil spray
- Black pepper

Instructions:
Heat a heavy based large saucepan and add a couple of sprays of rapeseed oil. Add the onion, garlic and chilli cook gently until softened – about 2-3 minutes.

Add the garam masala, turmeric, cumin seeds and seitan pieces. Stir and cook for a further 2-3 minutes.

Add the tomatoes and lentil soup. Bring to the boil then reduce the heat and simmer (stirring occasionally), cook for a further 10-15 minutes until the sauce has thickened.

Serve in a warmed bowl topped with freshly ground black pepper and the fresh coriander leaves.

Aubergine, Chickpea and Quorn Tagine

Kcal	Fat	Saturates	Carbs	Sugars	Protein	Fibre	Salt
230	5.5g	0.8g	25.5g	9.9g	21.2g	14.6g	2.2g

Serves: 2   **Prep time:** 5 minutes   **Cooking time:** 20 minutes

Ingredients:
- 1 small aubergine, diced
- 200g Quorn vegan pieces
- 1x210g can of chickpeas, drained
- 1x400g can of chopped tomatoes
- 2 garlic cloves, peeled and diced
- 1 small red onion
- 3 tsp tagine paste
- Juice and zest of 1 large orange

Instructions:

Heat a nonstick frying pan and dry-fry the onions and garlic until soft and lightly coloured

Add the aubergine and tagine paste, and continue to cook to brown the aubergine. Add the Quorn pieces and cook for a further 1-2 minutes

Add the tomatoes, orange juice, zest, chickpeas and stock cube. Cover with a lid and simmer gently for 30 minutes. Serve straight away.

Spicy Seitan and Noodle Soup

Kcal	Fat	Saturates	Carbs	Sugars	Protein	Fibre	Salt
275	2g	0.3g	25.7g	3.5g	40.3g	2.9g	1.2g

Serves: 1   **Prep time:** 5 minutes   **Cooking time:** 15 minutes

Ingredients:
- 250ml vegetable stock
- 50g seitan, diced
- 50g cooked leftover potatoes, diced
- 50g cooked leftover carrots
- 10g dry spaghetti
- ½ tsp dried chilli flakes
- Soy sauce
- Black pepper
- A little fresh parsley for garnish (optional)

Instructions:

Place the stock into a saucepan and bring to the boil. Break the spaghetti pasta into 2cm lengths and add to the boiling stock. Reduce the heat slightly and cook for 10 minutes.

Add the diced seitan, potatoes, carrots and chilli flakes to the stock and pasta. Reduce the heat to a simmer and cook for a further 4-5 minutes.

Season with a little soy sauce freshly ground black pepper and fresh parsley (if using) and serve straight away.

Chinese Style Tempeh

Kcal	Fat	Saturates	Carbs	Sugars	Protein	Fibre	Salt
458	5.6g	0.5g	36.5g	6.3g	69.5g	2.5g	1.3g

Serves: 1   **Prep time:** 5 minutes   **Marinating time:** 1 hour
Cooking time: 5-10 minutes

Ingredients:
- 120g tempeh – cut into 1cm cubes
- 1 tablespoon golden syrup
- 2 teaspoons dark soy sauce
- 1 teaspoon sesame oil
- ½ tsp Chinese five spice

Instructions:
Place the golden syrup, dark soy sauce, sesame oil and Chinese five spice into a medium bowl and mix together.

Add the cubed tempeh, and stir so that it is completely coated in the marinade.

Cover the bowl with cling film, and refrigerate for at least 1 hour (this can be done overnight if you prefer).

Heat a medium frying pan until hot, and the tempeh cubes and fry for 5-10 minutes until heated through and the syrup starts to caramelise, pour over any remaining marinade and serve straight away.

Great served with rice or noodles.

Tomato, Caper and Olive Tempeh

Kcal	Fat	Saturates	Carbs	Sugars	Protein	Fibre	Salt
458	5.6g	0.5g	36.5g	6.3g	69.5g	2.5g	1.3g

Serves: 2   **Prep time:** 5 minutes   **Cooking time:** 15 minutes

Ingredients:
- 250g tempeh, cut into 1cm cubes
- 300g tomato passata
- 1 tsp tomato puree
- 8 green olives, stones removed and sliced
- 2 tsps capers
- A few fresh basil leaves
- 1 small garlic clove, peeled and diced
- Rapeseed oil spray

Instructions:
Heat a frying pan and add a couple of sprays of rapeseed oil. Add the garlic and cook for 1-2 minutes.

Add the tomato passata, tomato puree, olives and capers to the pan and reduce the heat to a gentle simmer, cook for a further 1-2 minutes.

Add the cubed tempeh to the frying pan and stir to coat in the sauce, cook for 5-6 minutes until the tempeh is hot and the sauce has thickened slightly.

Serve straight away on a warmed plate with a few fresh basil leaves on top.

Great with pasta or fresh bread.

Sides and Sauces

Hassleback Baked Sweet Potato

Kcal	Fat	Saturates	Carbs	Sugars	Protein	Fibre	Salt
187	1.6g	0.3g	38.3g	10.3g	2.3g	4.6g	0.66g

Serves: 1   **Prep time:** 5 minutes **Cooking time:** 40 minutes

Ingredients:
- 1 sweet potato (approx. 180g with skin)
- 1 clove of garlic, cut in half
- Rapeseed oil spray
- Salt and black pepper

Instructions:
Preheat the oven to 200C, 400F, Gas Mark 6.

Wipe clean the potato and then dry (do not peel). Rub the outside with the cut garlic clove (discard the garlic).

Cut slices into the potato 3 mm apart and about 8 mm from the bottom. Place on a baking tray.

Spray with a little rapeseed oil, and season with the salt and black pepper and place in the top part of the oven.

Serve hot.

Pearl Couscous Salad

Kcal	Fat	Saturates	Carbs	Sugars	Protein	Fibre	Salt
227	3.5g	0.3g	42.5g	4.8g	8.3g	3.1g	0.89g

Serves: 1 **Prep time:** 5 minutes **Cooking time:** 10 minutes

Ingredients:
- 50g dry pearl couscous
- 6 cherry tomatoes, quartered
- 10g dried cranberries
- 50g cucumber, diced
- ½ tsp dried mixed herbs
- Zest and juice of 1 lime
- 1 vegetable stock cube
- Small handful of fresh parsley, chopped
- Rapeseed oil spray
- Salt and black pepper to season

Instructions:
Add a couple of sprays of the oil into a saucepan and heat. Add the couscous and gently fry for a couple of minutes until the couscous smells toasted, add the dried cranberries then cover with water and add the stock cube. Bring to the boil and simmer for 6-8 minutes, or until the couscous is just tender.

Using a sieve, drain the couscous and transfer to a bowl. Stir in the remaining ingredients.

Season with a little salt and pepper.

Serve straight away or store in the fridge for up to 24 hours.

Couscous with Fruit and Nuts

Kcal	Fat	Saturates	Carbs	Sugars	Protein	Fibre	Salt
308	9.4g	0.7g	48.5g	11.7g	9.2g	1.9g	0.88g

Serves: 2   **Prep time:** 5 minutes

Ingredients:
- 100g couscous (dry weight)
- 300ml hot vegetable stock
- 3 dried apricots, chopped
- 1 tbsp sultanas
- 5 almonds, chopped
- 15g pine nut kernels

Instructions:
Put the couscous, chopped apricots and sultanas in a mixing bowl and pour over the hot vegetable stock. Mix well, then cover with clingfilm and leave for 2-3 minutes until the water has been absorbed.

Add the almond and pine kernels to the couscous and mix together well.

Serve straight away or store in the fridge for up to 24 hours.

Cauliflower Hash Browns

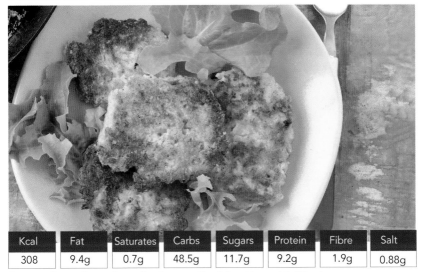

Kcal	Fat	Saturates	Carbs	Sugars	Protein	Fibre	Salt
308	9.4g	0.7g	48.5g	11.7g	9.2g	1.9g	0.88g

Serves: 2 **Prep time:** 5 minutes **Cooking time:** 10-15 minutes

Ingredients:
- 280g cauliflower florets
- 2 spring onions, finely sliced
- 1 medium egg, beaten
- Freshly ground black pepper and a pinch of salt
- Rapeseed oil spray

Instructions:
Grate the cauliflower florets into a medium size bowl, add the beaten egg, sliced spring onions and the salt and black pepper. Mix together well.

Heat a medium sized frying pan. Add a couple of sprays of the rapeseed oil then using a spoon add ¼ of the mixture to the pan and shape into a rough circle, and repeat with the remaining mixture, making 4 hash browns in total.

Cook for 5-7 minutes until golden brown, spray the tops with another spray of the oil and gently flip over. Cook for another 5-6 minutes.

Serve hot.

Quick Tomato Salsa

Kcal	Fat	Saturates	Carbs	Sugars	Protein	Fibre	Salt
550	20g	4.5g	44g	22g	1.5g	1.5g	3.2g

Serves: 1 **Prep time:** 5 minutes **Cooking time:** 25-30 minutes

Ingredients:
- 120g very ripe fresh tomatoes deseeded
- 1 spring onion, cleaned and roughly chopped
- 1 tbsp fresh coriander – roughly chopped
- 1 small clove of garlic, peeled
- Pinch of salt
- 1 small green chilli

Instructions:
Place all of the above ingredients into a blender – blend for 10-20 seconds or until the desired texture is obtained.

Leave in the fridge for at least 1 hour to get the best flavour.

Serve straight away or keep in the fridge for up to 2 days.

Courgette Bombs

Kcal	Fat	Saturates	Carbs	Sugars	Protein	Fibre	Salt
27	1.7g	0.7g	0.6g	0.5g	2.4g	0g	0.14g

Makes: 12 **Prep time:** 5 minutes **Cooking time:** 12-15 minutes

Ingredients:
- 400g courgettes, grated and excess water pressed out
- 2 medium eggs, beaten
- 25g pecorino cheese
- Pinch of black pepper

Instructions:
Preheat the oven to 200C, 400F, Gas Mark 6.

Place all of the ingredients into a bowl and gently mix together, until combined.

Divide into 12 portions, and shape into balls. Place on a baking tray lined with baking parchment and place in the oven, cook for 12-15 mins until they start to go golden brown.

Remove from the oven and carefully trim back any egg leakage.

Eat hot or cold. These will keep in the fridge for 2-3 days.

Quick and Easy Flatbreads

Kcal	Fat	Saturates	Carbs	Sugars	Protein	Fibre	Salt
167	2.4g	1.5g	30g	1.3g	6.8g	1.5g	0.74g

Makes: 4   **Prep time:** 25 minutes   **Cooking time:** 5 minutes

Ingredients:
- 150g self-raising flour
- 150g Greek yoghurt
- ½ tsp baking powder

Instructions:
Add the flour, baking powder and Greek yoghurt to a mixing bowl and mix together with a spoon, then use clean hands to bring everything together to a rough dough.

Dust the work surface with a little flour and place the dough on the surface and knead for 1-2 two minutes. Leave the dough to rest for 15-20 minutes.

Cut the dough into four pieces and roll each piece into a circle roughly the size of a side plate.

Heat a large heavy based frying pan until its very hot.

Add one of the flatbreads to the hot frying pan and cook for 1-2 minutes on each side or until it starts to puff up. It will be very hot so use kitchen tongs to turn the flat bread. Repeat with the rest of the dough.

TIP
This base works very well as a quick and simple pizza base.

Simple Tomato & Chilli Jam

Kcal	Fat	Saturates	Carbs	Sugars	Protein	Fibre	Salt
46	0.2g	0g	10.8g	10.6g	0.4g	0.4g	0.14g

Makes: 8 **Prep time:** 5 minutes **Cooking time:** 40 minutes

Ingredients:
- 1x200g can of chopped tomatoes
- 75g dark muscovado sugar
- 1 small red onion – peeled and quartered
- 2 red chillies
- 1 tbsp Balsamic vinegar
- Rapeseed oil spray
- A pinch of sea salt and black pepper to taste

Instructions:
Remove the tops from both the chillies and place in a blender with the onion and blend until very finely chopped.

Heat a small heavy based frying pan until hot. Add a couple of sprays of the rapeseed oil and add the onion and chilli mixture to the pan and cook for 2-3 minutes until softened, stirring continuously.

Add the balsamic vinegar to the pan and cook for a further minute.

Add the sugar, stir until fully mixed in. Cook until mixture starts to boil, turn the heat down slightly to control the boiling, cook for a further 5 mins, then add the salt and a little black pepper.

Gently pour in the chopped tomatoes and stir. Bring back to the boil then reduce the heat to achieve a simmer. Cook for a further 30 minutes or until the excess liquid has been absorbed and a thick consistency has been achieved.

Allow to cool completely then store in the fridge in an airtight container – this will keep for 7 days.

This is great with a burger, in a cheese sandwich, as a pizza topping, a quick pasta sauce (thin it down with a tiny amount of hot water) and so much more!

Egg Fried Rice

Kcal	Fat	Saturates	Carbs	Sugars	Protein	Fibre	Salt
286	6.8g	1.6g	44g	5g	3.3g	12.9g	0.22g

Serves: 1   **Prep time:** 5 minutes   **Cooking time:** 20 minutes

Ingredients:
- 45g basmati rice (dry weight)
- 25g frozen peas
- 25g frozen sweetcorn
- ½ small onion, peeled and diced
- 1 small egg - beaten
- Rapeseed oil spray

Instructions:
Cook the rice in a pan of boiling water 2 minutes before the rice is cooked add the peas and sweetcorn, cook for two more minutes drain.

Heat a non-stick frying pan and add a couple of sprays of the rapeseed oil. Add the onion and cook for 2-3 minutes. Add the rice/pea/sweet corn mixture, stir and cook for a further 1-2 minutes.

Move the rice to the edge of the pan and add another spray of oil to the visible pan area, pour in the egg, leave for 10 seconds then mix quickly into the rice mixture until the rice is coated.

Serve straight away.

Basic Tomato Pasta Sauce

Kcal	Fat	Saturates	Carbs	Sugars	Protein	Fibre	Salt
56	0.5g	0g	10.2g	9.1g	3.2g	2.3g	0.1g

Serves: 2   **Prep time:** 2 minutes   **Cooking time:** 3-5 minutes

Ingredients:
- 1x400g can chopped tomatoes
- 3 tsp tomato puree
- 1 ½ tsp Italian mixed herbs
- Freshly ground black pepper
- Dash of Worcestershire sauce (optional)

Instructions:
Place all of the ingredients in a blender, blend for 30 seconds.

Place in a small saucepan, bring to the boil, then reduce to a simmer for 2 minutes serve with pasta.

TIP
- If using in a Bolognese or lasagne then there is no need to cook it separately.
- Double up on the tomato puree, and this makes a great pizza topping - no need to cook before using.

Sweet Potato Hummous

Kcal	Fat	Saturates	Carbs	Sugars	Protein	Fibre	Salt
119	6g	0.9g	13g	4.8g	4g	2g	0.05g

Serves: 6   **Prep time:** 5 minutes

Ingredients:
- 200g cooked sweet potato, cooled
- 50g Tahini paste
- 1x210g can of chickpeas in water, drained
- 3 cloves of garlic peeled
- 1 tsp ground cumin
- Juice and zest from 1 lime
- Pinch of salt
- ½ tsp paprika, for serving

Instructions:
Place all of the ingredients into a blender or food processor and blend until the desired consistency is achieved.

Transfer to a bowl or jar, sprinkle over the paprika and chill until required.

This will keep for 24-48 hours in the fridge.

Avocado Fries

Kcal	Fat	Saturates	Carbs	Sugars	Protein	Fibre	Salt
263	15.7g	3.4g	23.6g	0.7g	8.3g	1.9g	0.13g

Serves: 2   **Prep time:** 5 minutes   **Cooking time:** 10-15 minutes

Ingredients:
- 1 medium avocado
- 20g plain flour
- 1 egg (see tip below to make this vegan friendly)
- 40g dry semolina or use 50g stale breadcrumbs
- 1 tsp smoked paprika
- Freshly ground black pepper
- Rapeseed oil spray

Instructions:
Pre-heat the oven to 210C, 475F, Gas Mark 9.

Slice the avocados in half, and then slice lengthwise into wedges.

Crack the egg into a small bowl and beat for 1 minute.

Place the flour into a separate bowl and add the smoked paprika and black pepper, stir to combine.

Place the semolina into a small bowl. Line a baking tray with baking parchment.

Dip a slice of avocado into the flour, then into the egg and then into the semolina, making sure it is evenly coated. Place the avocado slice on the baking tray and repeat until all the slices have been covered.

TIP
Mix 1 tbsp flaxmeal with 3 tbsp of hot water to replace the egg, this will make the recipe vegan friendly.

Spicy Sweet Potato Chips

Kcal	Fat	Saturates	Carbs	Sugars	Protein	Fibre	Salt
157	1.2g	0.2g	36.5g	9.8g	2.8g	6g	0.33g

Serves: 2   **Prep time:** 5 minutes   **Cooking time:** 15-20 minutes

Ingredients:
- 2 large sweet potatoes (approx. 180g each)
- 1 tbsp of any spice mix – your choice (I love 1tsp smoked paprika mixed with
- 1 tsp Cajun spices and a touch of black pepper)

Instructions:
Preheat the oven to 200C , 400F, gas Mark 6.

Cut the sweet potatoes into wedges and place in bowl (don't pat the wedges dry as the moisture will help the spice mix stick).

Add the spices mix them together so the wedges are evenly coated in the spices.

Place the wedges onto a non-stick baking tray.

Bake at the top of the oven for 15- 20 minutes until crisp.

Serve straight away.

Quick Smoked Salmon Pate

Kcal	Fat	Saturates	Carbs	Sugars	Protein	Fibre	Salt
169	8.2g	2.6g	3.7g	3.6g	20.1g	0.3g	2.2g

Serves: 2   **Prep time:** 5 minutes

Ingredients:
- 120g smoked salmon
- 90g extra light cream cheese
- 30g Greek yoghurt (5% fat)
- ½ tsp creamed horseradish
- 2 tsps chopped chives
- Black pepper to season

Instructions:
Place all of the ingredients except the chives into a blender and blend until an almost smooth texture is achieved.

Spoon the mixture into a bowl add the chopped chives and stir and season to taste with the black pepper.

Use straight away or store in the fridge for 24 hours.

Simple Vegetable Rice

Kcal	Fat	Saturates	Carbs	Sugars	Protein	Fibre	Salt
221	1.2g	0.2g	45.1g	2.3g	6.8g	3.8g	0.5g

Serves: 2   **Prep time:** 5 minutes   **Cooking time:** 15-20 minutes

Ingredients:
- 100g basmati rice
- 160g frozen mixed vegetables; such as peas, peppers, carrots, sweetcorn etc.
- 1 vegetable stock cube
- Freshly ground black pepper

Instructions:
Three quarters fill a medium sized saucepan with water and add the stock cube. Bring to the boil stirring occasionally to ensure the stock cube has dissolved.

Add the basmati rice to the water and cook for 10-12 minutes.

Add the frozen vegetables to the rice, bring back to the boil and cook for a further 3-4 minutes.

Drain and serve.

Over-night Slow Roasted Tomatoes

Kcal	Fat	Saturates	Carbs	Sugars	Protein	Fibre	Salt
29	1.2g	0.1g	3.9g	3.6g	0.7g	1.6g	0.76g

Serves: 4   **Prep time:** 5 minutes   **Cooking time:** 4 minutes

Ingredients:
- 500g ripe tomatoes
- Rapeseed oil spray
- Pinch sea salt
- 2 sprigs fresh thyme - optional

Instructions:
Pre-heat the oven to 220C, 475 F, Gas Mark 9.

Line a heavy baking tray with parchment.

Quarter the tomatoes and lay them skin side down on the baking tray in one even layer.

Spray lightly with the oil spray and sprinkle over the sea salt and fresh thyme if using.

Place them onto the top shelf in the oven and cook for 4 minutes, turn the oven off and leave the tomatoes to cook in the residual heat for at least 5-6 hours or ideally overnight.

When the tomatoes are cooked, transfer them to a plastic airtight container and store in the fridge.

They will keep for 4-5 days.

TIP
Amazing served in salads, in a tuna sandwich or just on their own as a quick snack.

Mushroom Rice

Kcal	Fat	Saturates	Carbs	Sugars	Protein	Fibre	Salt
233	1.5g	0.2g	46.3g	1.3g	5.4g	1.4g	0.2g

Serves: 1 **Prep time:** 5 minutes **Cooking time:** 25-30 minutes

Ingredients:
- 60g basmati rice (dry weight)
- 80g button mushrooms sliced
- 1tsp Worcestershire sauce
- Black pepper
- Rapeseed oil spray
- A few parsley leaves – optional

Instructions:
Bring a pan of water to the boil and add the rice.

In the meantime, heat a small frying pan, add a couple of sprays of the rapeseed oil and then add the mushrooms, Worcestershire sauce and a little black pepper and cook for 4-5 minutes until softened. Remove from the heat and set aside.

Drain the rice as soon as it is cooked and transfer it to the pan with the mushrooms in it, stir gently to combine, season with a little black pepper and transfer the mushroom rice to a warmed bowl.

Sprinkle with a little fresh parsley (optional).

TIP
This rice is great on its own with grilled beef steak, chicken or salmon.

Pea and Mint Puree

Kcal	Fat	Saturates	Carbs	Sugars	Protein	Fibre	Salt
62	1g	0.4g	7.8g	4.3g	5.6g	3.4g	0.27g

Serves: 6   **Prep time:** 5 minutes   **Cooking time:** 10 minutes

Ingredients:
- 375g frozen garden peas
- 100g reduced-fat cream cheese
- 1 vegetable stock cube
- 1 large tbsp handful of fresh mint leaves
- Freshly ground black pepper

Instructions:
Place the peas and stock cube in a saucepan and just cover with water. Bring to the boil for 2-3 minutes.

Drain the peas, then allow to cool.

Place the peas, cream cheese, mint and a little black pepper in a blender and blitz until almost smooth.

Serve straight away or keep in the fridge for up to 24 hours.

Sarah's BBQ Sauce

Kcal	Fat	Saturates	Carbs	Sugars	Protein	Fibre	Salt
51	0.1g	0g	12.3g	11.8g	0.4g	0.4g	0.42g

Serves: 5   **Prep time:** 5 minutes   **Cooking time:** 25 minutes

Ingredients:
- 120g tomato passata
- 50g dark muscovado sugar
- 1 tbsp Worcestershire sauce
- ¼ tsp black pepper
- 1 tbsp balsamic vinegar
- Pinch of sea salt

Instructions:
Place all of the ingredients into a small heavy based saucepan.

Gently bring to the boil then reduce the heat to a simmer stirring occasionally and cook for 25 minutes.

Remove from the heat and allow to cool. Pour into a glass jar and store in the fridge for 7-10 days.

Sweet

Fruity Waffles

Kcal	Fat	Saturates	Carbs	Sugars	Protein	Fibre	Salt
308	4.2g	1.5g	58g	14.5g	10.3g	3.2g	1g

Serves: 4   **Prep time:** 5 minutes   **Cooking time:** 15 minutes

Ingredients:
- 225g plain flour
- 300ml semi-skimmed milk
- 1 tsp vanilla extract
- 30g caster sugar
- 1 tsp bicarbonate of soda
- 1 medium egg
- Rapeseed oil spray
- 200g mixed fresh berries, such as raspberries and blueberries
- Pinch of icing sugar - optional

Instructions:
Combine the flour, sugar, baking powder and bicarbonate of soda in a mixing bowl. Add the egg and vanilla. Using a whisk, gradually pour in the milk, beating the mixture to a smooth, lump free batter.

Preheat a waffle iron or non-stick frying pan; lightly spray the waffle plate or pan with the rapeseed oil.

If using a frying pan, place the cutter in the pan. Spoon 3-4 tablespoons of the mixture into the iron or cutter and cook for 2 minutes. Flip it over and cook on the other side for a further 2 minutes.

Remove from the pan and keep warm. Repeat with the remaining mixture until you have four waffles.

Serve hot topped with the fresh berries and a dusting of icing sugar.

Chocolate, Almond and Coffee Ice Cream

Kcal	Fat	Saturates	Carbs	Sugars	Protein	Fibre	Salt
308	4.2g	1.5g	58g	14.5g	10.3g	3.2g	1g

Serves: 6/7   **Prep time:** 5 minutes **Cooking time:** 5 minutes
Freezing time: approx. 6 hours

Ingredients:
- 5 heaped tbsp (150g) of good quality cocoa powder
- 80g caster sugar
- 40g chopped almonds
- 300ml boiling water
- 100ml hot strong coffee
- 100ml Coconut milk
- 1 tsp vanilla essence
- 1 tbs of coffee liqueur or brandy

Instructions:
Place the cocoa & sugar in a saucepan. Slowly add the boiling water and hot coffee (mixing all the time) until all lumps have dissolved, then add the Coconut milk. Gently heat for 2-3 minutes on a hob - do not boil to ensure a smooth flavour.

Allow the mixture to cool completely and add the chopped almonds, vanilla essence and alcohol and stir until combined.

Pour into a plastic container, complete with lid and freeze for 2 hours, then stir thoroughly, re-freeze for a further 2 hours. Stir again and then freeze for a final two hours or until required.

This is best used within 2 weeks of making to retain flavour.

You can use this recipe in an ice-cream maker.

Banana Whip

Kcal	Fat	Saturates	Carbs	Sugars	Protein	Fibre	Salt
134	0.7g	0.5g	20.1g	18.3g	11.5g	1.3g	0.25g

Serves: 2   **Prep time:** 5 minutes plus 1 hour chilling

Ingredients:
- 2 medium ripe bananas
- 150g 0% fat Greek yoghurt
- 50g low fat cream cheese
- 2 drops of vanilla essence

Instructions:
Peel the bananas and place 1 ½ of the bananas into a medium mixing bowl, wrapping the remaining half in cling film and reserving for the garnish.

Mash the banana in the bowl until very soft and sloppy.

Stir in the yoghurt, cream cheese and vanilla extract.

Using a whisk, whisk for 2-3 minutes or until smooth and creamy.

Divide equally between two glass dessert dishes. Chill for 1-2 hours.

Just before serving, remove the remaining banana from the cling film and slice and divide equally between the two desserts and serve.

Apple and Almond Cake

Kcal	Fat	Saturates	Carbs	Sugars	Protein	Fibre	Salt
163	3.8g	0.6g	28.3g	15.8g	4.2g	1.3g	0.35g

Serves: 8　　**Prep time:** 5 minutes　　**Cooking time:** 20-25 minutes

Ingredients:
- 2 eating apples, such as pink lady
- 100g golden caster sugar (you can use white caster sugar)
- 130g self raising flour
- ½ tsp baking powder
- 30g ground almonds
- 100g apple puree or stewed apples (without added sugar)
- 2 medium eggs, lightly beaten
- Two drops of almond essence

Instructions:
Preheat the oven to 170C, 325F, Gas Mark 3.

Peel the apples, core and dice into cm cubes, and sprinkle on to the bottom of a 20cm silicone round sandwich mould (if using a metal tin, line with baking parchment).

Mix together the apple puree with the sugar, 2 beaten eggs, self raising flour, ground almonds and almond essence in a mixing bowl, then pour over the diced apples.

Bake in the oven for 20-25 minutes, until risen and golden in colour.

Allow to cool slightly, before turning out. Serve warm or cold.

TIP
Swap the flour to gluten free flour if you are following a gluten free lifestyle.

Banana and Chocolate Whip

Kcal	Fat	Saturates	Carbs	Sugars	Protein	Fibre	Salt
121	1.7g	1g	14g	12g	12.3g	0.7g	0.1g

Serves: 2   **Prep time:** 5 minutes plus 1 hour chilling

Ingredients:
- 1 ripe large banana
- 200g 0% fat Greek yoghurt
- 15g cocoa powder

Instructions:

Peel the banana and place into a medium mixing bowl and mash until very soft and sloppy. Stir in the cocoa powder and yoghurt.

Using a whisk, whisk for 2-3 minutes or until smooth and creamy.

Divide equally between two glass dessert dishes. Chill for 1-2 hours.

Coconut and Chia Seed Dessert

Kcal	Fat	Saturates	Carbs	Sugars	Protein	Fibre	Salt
138	6.5g	1g	10.9g	10.5g	5.2g	8.8g	0.45g

Serves: 1   **Prep time:** 5 minutes plus 1-2 hours standing time

Ingredients:
- 160g canned coconut milk
- 50g mixed fresh berries
- 1 ½ tbsp's chia seeds
- Dash of vanilla extract

Instructions:
Mix the coconut milk, vanilla and chia seeds together and pour into a tumbler. Leave to thicken for 1-2 hours in the fridge or for better results overnight.

Just before serving top with the mixed berries.

TIP
This makes a perfect breakfast too!

Date and Nut Energy Balls

Kcal	Fat	Saturates	Carbs	Sugars	Protein	Fibre	Salt
99	7g	1g	5.6g	0.01g	2.8g	0.5g	0.01g

Makes: 8   **Prep time:** 5 minutes

Ingredients:
- 120g medjool dates, pitted
- 30g ground almonds
- 30g walnut halves
- 25g plain cashews
- 1 tsp chia seeds
- 1tsp flax seeds
- 1 ½ tsp dark cocoa powder

Instructions:
Place the walnuts, cashews, chia and flaxseeds in a food processor and blitz until a fine crumb.

Add the ground almonds and cocoa powder and blitz for a further 30 seconds.

Add the dates and the vanilla extract and blitz until it forms a sticky dough.

Dived the mixture into 8 portions and roll each portion into a ball and place on a tray covered in baking parchment.

Place them in the fridge for 30 minutes to set, then transfer to a plastic container and store in the fridge for up to 7 days.

Not suitable for freezing.

Sarah's Affogato

Kcal	Fat	Saturates	Carbs	Sugars	Protein	Fibre	Salt
167	6.6g	4.2g	24.4g	21.7g	2.7g	0.2g	0.13g

Serves: 1   **Prep time:** 3 minutes

Ingredients:
- 1 scoop (80g) vanilla ice cream, this can be dairy free
- 1 shot of hot espresso or very strong coffee (60ml)
- 2 tsps coffee liqueur such as Kahlua or Baileys

Instructions:
Place the coffee liqueur in the bottom of a tumbler or small glass dish.

Top with the scoop of ice cream.

Pour over the hot coffee and serve immediately.

TIP
You can omit the liqueur if you wish or try brandy or bourbon for a slightly different flavour.

Banana and Granola Stuffed Baked Apples

Kcal	Fat	Saturates	Carbs	Sugars	Protein	Fibre	Salt
163	3.8g	0.6g	28.3g	15.8g	4.2g	1.3g	0.35g

Serves: 3   **Prep time:** 5 minutes   **Cooking time:** 15-20 minutes

Ingredients:
- 3 eating apples
- 1 small ripe banana, peeled
- 50g granola or muesli
- ½ tsp mixed spice
- A little honey or golden syrup for serving (optional)

Instructions:
Preheat the oven to 180C, 350F, Gas Mark 4.

Cut the top off the apples and reserve for the lids. Using a teaspoon or apple corer carefully remove the core of the apples and discard, ensuring you don't break through the skin.

Place the hollowed out apples in a small shallow oven-proof dish.

Place the peeled banana into a small bowl and mash until very soft and sloppy. Stir in the granola and mixed spice.

Divide the mixture equally between the three apples and place the apple lids on top and bake in the oven for 15 – 20 minutes.

Serve drizzled with a little honey or golden syrup (use golden syrup to make vegan).

TIP
These are great hot or cold and make a good alternative for breakfast and will keep in the fridge for 2 days.

Oat, Banana, Apple and Walnut Cookies

Kcal	Fat	Saturates	Carbs	Sugars	Protein	Fibre	Salt
230	9g	1.1g	32.3g	8.3g	5.6g	3.9g	0g

Makes: 4   **Prep time:** 5 minutes   **Cooking time:** 15 minutes

Ingredients:
- 140g porridge oats
- 1 small very ripe banana
- 1 eating apple, grated (skin on)
- 6 walnut halves, finely chopped
- ½ tsp cinnamon
- 1 tbsp honey

Instructions:
Preheat the oven to 165C, 325F, Gas Mark 3. Line a baking tray with baking parchment.

In a bowl mash the banana flesh until it's gooey, then stir in the honey, grated apple, cinnamon and walnuts. Add the oats and mix until all the ingredients are combined.

Divide the mixture into four equal portions. Roll each portion into a ball and gently flatten until about 1cm thick. Place in the oven and cook for 15 minutes or until firm to touch.

Remove from the oven and allow to cool.

Store in an airtight container - will keep for 3-4 days.

TIP
Swap the honey to golden syrup to make the recipe vegan.

Chocolate and Chia Seed Dessert

Kcal	Fat	Saturates	Carbs	Sugars	Protein	Fibre	Salt
230	11.3g	1.3g	13.4g	11.8g	7.6g	9g	0.21g

Makes: 2   **Prep time:** 5 minutes plus 1-2 hours chilling time

Ingredients:
- 300ml Alpro Almond Dark Chocolate longlife drink
- 45g chia seeds
- 50g fresh raspberries
- 10g flaked almonds

Instructions:
Mix the almond chocolate drink and chia seeds together in a bowl and then pour into two tumblers or glass dessert dishes. Leave to thicken for 1-2 hours in the fridge or for better results overnight.

Just before serving top with the raspberries and flaked almonds.

Layered Strawberry Cheesecake

Kcal	Fat	Saturates	Carbs	Sugars	Protein	Fibre	Salt
163	5.8g	2.8g	20g	13g	7.4g	3.7g	0.46g

Serves: 1   **Prep time:** 5 minutes   **Cooking time:** 10 minutes
Chilling time: approx. 20 minutes

Ingredients:
- A small handful of very ripe strawberries
- 1tsp honey
- 1 tbsp Greek yoghurt
- 1 tbsp low-fat cream cheese
- Dash of vanilla essence (optional)
- 1 digestive biscuit- why not swap for a chocolate biscuit as an alternative!

Instructions:
Set aside a couple of strawberry's for the topping and place the rest in a small saucepan with the honey and a tbsp. of water.   Gently bring to a medium heat (do not allow to boil) and cook for 3-5 minutes until the strawberries have collapsed, using a wooden spoon mash them until a rough puree has been achieved. Set aside and leave to cool for 20 minutes.

In another bowl add the yoghurt, cream cheese and vanilla essence. Mix together until smooth.

Place the biscuit in a blender, and blend until breadcrumb like in consistency.

Take a glass tumbler, place the crumbed biscuit in the bottom, then top with half of the cream cheese mixture. Top the cream cheese mixture with half of the strawberry sauce. Repeat the process with the remaining cream cheese mixture and the finally the last of the strawberry sauce.

Decorate with the strawberries.

Chill for 15 - 20 minutes before serving.

Cocoa and Raisin Energy Balls

Kcal	Fat	Saturates	Carbs	Sugars	Protein	Fibre	Salt
85	4.4g	1.1g	8.7g	3.7g	2.6g	1.2g	0.07g

Makes: 18   **Prep time:** 5 minutes

Ingredients:
- 120g porridge oats
- 120g peanut butter
- 1 tbsp honey or golden syrup
- 2 tsp flaxseeds
- 2 tsp chia seeds
- 3 tsp dark cocoa powder
- 60g raisins
- ½ tsp vanilla extract

Instructions:

Place all of the ingredients in a large mixing bowl. Stir to combine.

If the mixture seems too wet, add a bit more oats. If it's too dry, add a bit more peanut butter. It should be a sticky dough that holds together.

Place the bowl in the refrigerator for 30 minutes to set.

Divide the mixture into 18 equal portions, and roll into balls, store in an airtight container in the fridge.

These will keep for 10-12 days in the fridge or they can be frozen for up to two months.

Quick Berry Ice Cream

Kcal	Fat	Saturates	Carbs	Sugars	Protein	Fibre	Salt
122	3.8g	2.2g	12.7g	8.4g	6.8g	4.2g	0.06g

Serves: 1   **Prep time:** 5 minutes

Ingredients:
- 240g frozen berries - any combination
- 130g chilled 5% fat Greek yoghurt
- Dash of vanilla essence (optional)

Instructions:
Place all of the ingredients into a blender and blend straight away until the desired consistency is achieved.

The frozen berries help to freeze the yoghurt so that the ice-cream can be eaten straight away, or you can pop the ice-cream into a plastic container and freeze until required.

This will keep in the freezer for up to two months.

Chocolate Mallow Mousse

Kcal	Fat	Saturates	Carbs	Sugars	Protein	Fibre	Salt
241	4.1g	2.8g	41.9g	32.2g	7.8g	0g	0.09g

Serves: 1   **Prep time:** 5 minutes plus 1-2 hours chilling time
Cooking time: 15 minutes

Ingredients:
- 100g mini marshmallows
- 100g 5% fat Greek yoghurt
- 20g cocoa powder

Instructions:
Bring to the boil a small saucepan a third filled with water. Place a small non-metallic bowl on top and add the marshmallows to the bowl. Reduce the heat to a simmer, and cook the marshmallows gently until they have melted.

Remove from the heat, take the bowl off the pan of water. Add the cocoa powder to the melted marshmallows, stir to combine then leave to cool for 5 minutes.

Stir the Greek yoghurt gently into the chocolate marshmallow mix then divide the mixture between two glass tumblers. Chill for 1-2 hours until lightly set, serve straight away.

This dessert is perfect as an occasional treat!

Banana Pops

Kcal	Fat	Saturates	Carbs	Sugars	Protein	Fibre	Salt
241	4.1g	2.8g	41.9g	32.2g	7.8g	0g	0.09g

Makes: 6   **Prep time:** 5 minutes   **Freezing time:** approx. 3-4 hours

Ingredients:
- 3 medium ripe bananas
- 100g dark chocolate
- 6 mini wooden skewers or lolly pop sticks

Instructions:
Peel the bananas and cut in half (width ways).

Push a wooden skewer (trim the sharp end to make it flat) halfway up into each of the banana halves and then place the bananas onto a small tray that is lined with baking parchment.

Place the bananas into the freezer and freeze for 3-4 hours or until solid.

Just before removing the bananas from the freezer, gently melt the chocolate in a glass bowl over some hot water.

Once the chocolate has melted remove from the heat. Take the bananas from the freezer and gently dip each one into the chocolate, working quickly and place them back on the tray.

Return to the freezer for at least 15 minutes - these will keep in the freezer for 1 month.

TIP
Add a few chopped nuts or desiccated coconut to the melted chocolate before dipping the bananas.

Almond and Poppy Seed Muffins

Kcal	Fat	Saturates	Carbs	Sugars	Protein	Fibre	Salt
224	10.4g	1.9g	25.7g	13.8g	7.4g	1.2g	0.27g

Serves: 6   **Prep time:** 10 minutes   **Cooking time:** 25 minutes

Ingredients:
- 80g caster sugar
- 50g self-raising flour
- 50g wholemeal flour
- 3 large eggs
- 30g reduced-fat margarine
- 25g ground almonds
- 1 tsp poppy seeds
- 20g flaked almonds
- A couple of drops of almond extract

Instructions:
Preheat oven to 220C /425F /Gas Mark 7.

In a large bowl, whisk together the eggs, sugar, low fat margarine and almond extract together for 1-2 minutes until it goes a little frothy.

Gently fold in the flour, ground almonds and poppy seeds.

Divide the muffin mixture between a 6 holes non-stick muffin tin.

Scatter over the almonds and then bake for 20-25 mins until puffed up and golden.

Serve warm or leave to cool, best eaten the same day.

You can freeze these as soon as they have cooled, and they will keep in the freezer for about 1 month.

Quick Chocolate Orange Crumble Surprise

Kcal	Fat	Saturates	Carbs	Sugars	Protein	Fibre	Salt
185	9.7g	5.5g	20.1g	12.2g	4.1g	1.6g	0.41g

Serves: 2   **Prep time:** 5 minutes

Ingredients:
- 200g Koko dairy free plain yogurt
- 2 tsp cocoa powder
- Nakd Cocoa Orange Bar
- 2 tsp porridge oats
- 50g fresh raspberries

Instructions:

Place the yogurt and the cocoa powder in a bowl and mix until combined, then divide between two wine glasses or tumblers.

Break the bar into several smaller pieces and place in a blender with the porridge oats and whizz until breadcrumbs.

Top the chocolate yogurt mix with the cereal bar crumble and then top with fresh raspberries.

Serve straight away.

Apricot Dream

Kcal	Fat	Saturates	Carbs	Sugars	Protein	Fibre	Salt
130	1.3g	0.9g	16g	16g	11.4g	1.4g	0.5g

Serves: 2   **Prep time:** 10 minutes

Ingredients:
- 1x410g can of apricots in fruit juice, drained
- 100g 0% fat Greek yoghurt
- 100g low-fat cream cheese
- ½ tsp vanilla extract
- A couple of chopped almonds for decoration (optional)

Instructions:
Place the drained apricots into a blender and blitz until smooth. Divide the mixture between two glasses.

Place the Greek yoghurt, cream cheese and vanilla extract into a bowl and beat until thick and creamy.

Carefully top the apricot puree with the creamy mixture and sprinkle over the chopped almonds if using. Serve straight away.

Blueberry, Almond and Oat Muffins

Kcal	Fat	Saturates	Carbs	Sugars	Protein	Fibre	Salt
193	6.9g	1.5g	28.1g	14.8g	5.1g	1g	0.6g

Serves: 6   **Prep time:** 10 minutes **Cooking time:** 25 minutes

Ingredients:
- 80g caster sugar
- 85g self raising flour
- 20g porridge oats + 1 tsp for decoration
- 2 large eggs
- 80g fresh blueberries
- 35g reduced-fat margarine
- 1 tbsp semi-skimmed milk
- 10g flaked almonds
- 1tsp baking powder
- A couple of drops of almond extract

Instructions:
Preheat oven to 200C/180C Fan/400F /Gas Mark 6.

In a large bowl, whisk together the eggs, sugar, low fat margarine, milk and almond extract together for 1-2 minutes until it goes a little frothy.

Gently fold in the flour, baking powder, blueberries and 20g of porridge oats Divide the muffin mixture between a 6 holes non-stick muffin tin.

Scatter over the almonds and remaining porridge oats and then bake for 20-25 mins until puffed up and golden.

Serve warm or leave to cool, best eaten the same day.

You can freeze these as soon as they have cooled, and they will keep in the freezer for about 1 month.

Kiwi and Granola Chia Dessert

Kcal	Fat	Saturates	Carbs	Sugars	Protein	Fibre	Salt
290	12.4g	2g	35g	20.3g	7.6g	7.5g	0.25g

Makes: 2   **Prep time:** 10 minutes plus 1-2 hours chilling time

Ingredients:
- 100ml hazelnut milk
- 1tbsp chia Seeds
- 1tbsp granola mix
- 2 kiwi fruit
- Dash vanilla essence

Instructions:
Mix the hazelnut milk, vanilla and chia seeds together in a small bowl and leave to thicken for 1-2 hours in the fridge.

Scoop out the flesh of 1 and a half of the kiwi fruits, discard the skins and blend the flesh in a mini food processor until a pulp.

Place the kiwi pulp in the bottom of a chilled glass and top with the chia seed mix and then sprinkle over the granola.

Peel, slice and the quarter the remaining kiwi fruit flesh and add to the dessert, serve straight away.

Blueberry Crumble

Kcal	Fat	Saturates	Carbs	Sugars	Protein	Fibre	Salt
275	5.6g	0.6g	51.5g	33.4g	5.3g	4.4g	0.02g

Serves: 2   **Prep time:** 5 minutes **Cooking time:** 20 minutes

Ingredients:
- 250g blueberries
- 1 tsp lemon juice freshly squeezed
- ½ tsp lemon zest of 1 lemon
- 20g caster sugar
- ½ tsp ground cinnamon

Ingredients for the crumble topping:
- 25g plain flour
- 25g soft brown sugar
- 25g porridge oats
- 15g ground almonds

Instructions:
Preheat the oven to 190C, Gas Mark 5, 375F

Toss blueberries with lemon juice, lemon zest, caster sugar and ground cinnamon. Divide equally between two ovenproof ramekin dishes.

For the crumble topping - In a bowl, combine the flour, brown sugar, porridge oats and ground almonds and mix until evenly combined.

Sprinkle the topping over the fruit evenly.

Bake 20-25 minutes at 180C. The blueberries should be bubbling at the edges and the topping and almonds should be golden brown.

Remove from the oven and allow to rest for 2-5 minutes before serving.

Recipe index

Indian Style Roasted Cauliflower Steaks 126
King Prawn and Asparagus Linguine 101
Kiwi and Granola Chia Dessert 180
Korean Beef with Noodles 82
Korean Chicken Noodles 87
Lamb Kofta 81
Layered Strawberry Cheesecake 171
Leftover Chicken and Noodle Soup 73
Leftover Chilli Con Carne Soup 70
Leftover Chilli Pasta Bake 85
Lemon Chicken with Fine Green Beans 88
Meatloaf Stuffed with Eggs 79
Mushroom and Banana Blossom Linguine 134
Mushroom and Cauliflower Pasta 130
Mushroom Rice 156
Oat, Banana, Apple and Walnut Cookies 169
Orange & Pineapple Glazed Gammon 80
Over-night Slow Roasted Tomatoes 155
Pan Fried Mackerel with a Potato and Beetroot Salad 107
Pea and Mint Puree 157
Pearl Couscous Salad 143
Potato, Mushroom and Pea Bake 127
Quick and Easy Flatbreads 147
Quick and Simple Pea Soup 115
Quick Berry Ice Cream 173
Quick Chocolate Orange Crumble Surprise 177
Quick Fish Curry 108
Quick Mexican Rice and Quinoa Salad 128
Quick Naan Bread Chicken and Sweetcorn Pizza 77
Quick Prawn and Courgette Rice 94
Quick Seitan Dhansak Curry 137
Quick Smoked Salmon Pate 154
Quick Sticky Chicken Kebabs 92
Quick Tomato Salsa 146
Quorn Marsala with Pasta 116
Rich Beef Casserole 90
Rich Chicken Chasseur 72
Rich Sausage and Mushroom Casserole 74
Roasted Ratatouille 120
Roasted Tomato and Pepper Soup 136
Salmon and Spinach Gnocchi 102
Salmon with a Warm Spinach and Chickpea Salad 99
Sarah's Affogato 167
Sarah's BBQ Sauce 158
Sausage Shakshuka 86

Simple Chicken Korma 78
Simple Fish and Pepper Stew 97
Simple Pork and Apple Stir-fry 83
Simple Quorn Korma 124
Simple Tomato & Chilli Jam 148
Simple Vegetable Rice 154
Smoky Bean & Sausage Stew 83
Smoky, Spicy, Sesame Chicken 69
Spicy Rainbow Stir-fry 131
Spicy Seitan and Noodle Soup 138
Spicy Sweet Potato Chips 153
Sticky Chicken Kebabs
Super Quick Sausage Bagel Pizza 75
Sweet and Sour Chicken with Rice 89
Sweet Potato and Okra Stew 125
Sweet Potato Hummus 151
Sweet Potato Soup 132
Sweet Potato with Spicy Salsa, Chickpeas and Avocado 119
Thai Style Fish Cakes 100
Three Bean Enchiladas 112
Tomato and Basil Gnocchi 114
Tomato and Olive Pasta 118
Tomato, Caper and Olive Tempeh 140
Tuna Rice Salad 105
Vegan Cheesy Cottage Pie 117
Vegetarian Cheesy Cottage Pie 133
Wild Mushroom Risotto 123